American Philosophical Society Library
Publication Number 14

Molecules, Cells, and Life:
An Annotated Bibliography of Manuscript Sources on Physiology, Biochemistry, and Biophysics, 1900–1960, in the Library of the American Philosophical Society

LILY E. KAY

American Philosophical Society Library • Philadelphia • 1989

Contents

Secondary Group: Manuscript Sources on Scientists in the Collections of Other Scientists   64

Published Sources Consulted for the Annotations   79

Index   85

Foreword

The Andrew W. Mellon Foundation, seeking to increase the scholarly usefulness of our collections and enrich the intellectual life of the Library, made a grant in 1982 to the American Philosophical Society establishing a fellowship program in bibliography, research scholarship, and staff development. The major thrust of the program is to provide fellowships for younger scholars who will prepare bibliographic studies on topics well represented in the Library's collections.

Dr. Lily E. Kay, assistant professor of the history of science at the University of Chicago, was a Mellon Fellow in Bibliography in 1986–88. During the first year of her residence in the Library, she completed her thoughtful description and analysis of our manuscript holdings in history of physiology, biochemistry, and biophysics for the period 1900–1960 which constitutes the core of this publication. The second half of her fellowship was devoted to assisting the Librarian in collection development in modern history of science.

Dr. Kay's education and professional career uniquely prepared her for the writing of *Molecules, Cells, and Life*. Prior to entering The Johns Hopkins University's history of science doctoral program, she did graduate work in both the physical and life sciences, and was also a research scientist in molecular biology at the Salk Institute, and in biochemistry and physiology at the University of Pittsburgh. All of her work as a Mellon Fellow has been characterized by intellectual rigor, a high degree of energy, and a continuing sense of curiosity.

We would like to acknowledge the generous support of The Andrew W. Mellon Foundation that made possible this work and those that will follow.

June 1988

Edward C. Carter II
Librarian
American Philosophical Society

Preface

From the time of its founding in 1743, America's oldest learned society, the American Philosophical Society, has promoted the practice and study of science as part of its commitment to useful knowledge. Broadly stated, the promotion of useful knowledge was reflected during the eighteenth and nineteenth centuries in vital cultural roles of the Society's membership and Library. The legacy of the American Philosophical Society in furthering knowledge has continued in the twentieth century through scientific meetings and interdisciplinary symposia, through publications, exhibits, the Library, and scholarly research.

It has been a pleasure and privilege to take part in the research activities at the APS Library through the support of an Andrew W. Mellon Foundation Fellowship. One of the strengths of the Library is its repository of manuscript records in American history; the collections in the history of American science contribute to this strength. Indeed, it has been gratifying to uncover such an abundance of scholarly material on the life sciences and to promote this body of useful knowledge through this annotated bibliography.

The project has benefited immeasurably from my association with the Library's staff. I am particularly grateful to Edward C. Carter II, Librarian, for his continuous scholarly encouragement and generous support. I am also indebted to Beth Carroll-Horrocks, Manuscript Librarian, for her expert guidance, resourceful assistance, and encouragement throughout the research and writing phases of this project. I thank David Rhees, Roy Goodman, Hedi Kyle, Susan Klepp, and Mark Linn for their support; and Nathan Reingold, Philip J. Pauly, and Robert E. Kohler for their critical comments.

PART ONE

Introduction

Introduction

The life sciences in the United States underwent major transformations during the first half of the twentieth century. That period saw the emergence of new disciplines and research schools, the rise of institutions, and the ascent of scientific leaders and powerful administrators. The coalescence of these intellectual and social trends propelled the United States from the periphery to the vanguard of biological research. While at the turn of the century students of the life sciences still traveled to Europe for their doctoral or post-doctoral education (mainly to Germany), by mid-century the nation's scientific institutions had become training grounds not only for new generations of Americans, but also for European students of the life sciences. The Library of the American Philosophical Society houses manuscript sources documenting important aspects of these intellectual and institutional developments. Over sixty collections at the Library deal directly with biological research in America in the twentieth century; with the exception of a handful of records of scientific societies and institutions, most of these collections are the personal papers of prominent researchers in various disciplines of the life sciences.

Scope of the Guide

This bibliographic guide to twenty-four manuscript collections is arranged around the disciplines of physiology, biochemistry, and biophysics. This organization of knowledge reflects that of the scientists, who generally identify themselves professionally in disciplinary terms. They frequently work in departments which reflect their disciplinary affiliation, belong to closely allied scientific societies, and tend to define the scope of their investigations within disciplinary boundaries. But while these broad fields—physiology, biochemistry, and biophysics—encompass the research and activities of the scientists described in this guide, they are necessarily oversimplified and somewhat arbitrary. Mapping the scientific landscape along disciplinary contours tends to ignore the richness, complexities, and fluidity of the life sciences.

Frequently, the boundaries which separate physiology, biochemistry, and biophysics are not only blurred, but also overlap with other fields such as botany, genetics, cytology, pathology, microbiology, immunology, and molecular biology. The research of biochemist Florence Siebert at the Phipps Institute in Philadelphia, for example, represents an overlap of biochemistry, bacteriology, and immunology. Francis J.W. Roughton's studies of hemoglobin and respiration at the Department of Colloid Sciences at Cambridge University and at the University of Pennsylvania fall within the domains of biochemistry, biophysics, and physiology. The quantitative investigations on plant cell membranes of Winthrop J.V. Osterhout of the Rockefeller Institute are as much a part of general physiology as of botany and biophysics; and Peyton Rous's work at the Institute on tumor viruses has been variously described as virology, microbiology, pathology, and physiology.

The decision to limit the annotations to physiology, biochemistry, and biophysics is arbitrary in yet another respect. Two major areas in the life sciences—medicine and genetics—have been deliberately left out. The exclusion of genetics is readily justified since an annotated bibliography of manuscript sources in genetics at the APS has recently been completed by H. Bentley Glass. Even in this instance it has been difficult to avoid an overlap. With the rise of molecular biology in the late 1930s, several geneticists began to focus their investigations on the physico-chemical nature of the gene, and research in genetics, microbiology, and biochemistry began to merge. The papers of geneticists Jack Schultz and Milislav Demerec, and those of biochemist Erwin Chargaff and virologist Peyton Rous reflect fundamental issues in physiological and biochemical genetics. These materials help document the early transition from classical genetics to molecular biology.

The exclusion of medicine has been more problematic. Some of the most fundamental studies in physiology, biochemistry, and biophysics have been conducted in medical institutions. William Mansfield Clark's investigations in physical biochemistry were carried out at the Johns Hopkins Medical School. The Rockefeller Institute for Medical Research, which has always fostered freedom of scientific inquiry, stimulated basic investigations in biochemistry, biophysics, and physiology that were only tangentially related to medical practice; the manuscript sources at the APS on Max Bergmann, Phoebus A.T. Levene, Winthrop J.V. Osterhout, and John H. Northrop exemplify this point. In fact, it would be difficult to name a single research problem in the life sciences that does not bear relevance to medicine. And indeed, most of the scientists in this guide have delivered Harvey Lectures at the New York Academy of Medicine.

What does link the scientists whose papers are covered in this annotated guide is their primary commitment to fundamental laboratory research in the life sciences. Their contributions to our understanding of normal and abnormal biological processes have been made by and large through research on the most basic level of cells and molecules. Taken together, these scientists represent some of the principal actors who have shaped the course of the life sciences in the United States in the twentieth century.

Format of the Guide

The annotated entries fall into two categories: Primary and Secondary. The Primary Group consists of twenty-four actual APS collections—twenty-two are the personal papers of life scientists, one collection (Cold Spring Harbor) contains institutional papers, and one collection (Anne Roe) consists of interviews. The Secondary Group consists of manuscript sources on twenty-one scientists whose personal papers are *not* at the Library, but on whom there are significant records in APS manuscript collections of other scientists (mainly scientists in the Primary Group). The criteria for "significant records" are based mainly on the quantity of material, although in some cases the importance of a small number of documents, in the judgment of the author, has merited separate entries. In fact, one purpose for creating the secondary group of entries is to call attention to significant sources which otherwise might be overlooked.

Throughout the bibliography, the primary entries (actual manuscript collections at APS) are designated with a *, while secondary entries (other APS manuscript sources) are designated with a **. For example, W.J. Robbins* refers to the Robbins Papers at the APS Library which are described in the Primary Group section; J.H. Northrop** refers to the materials on Northrop in various APS manuscript collections which are described under Northrop's name in the Secondary Group.

This notation system is also employed in the survey below. This historical overview places the manuscript sources within broad intellectual, institutional, and social contexts; the star system of notation highlights the links between members of the Secondary and Primary groups, as well as the relations of the life scientists to their wider milieu. The survey is appended with suggested research topics—seven areas that stand out as potentially fruitful studies based on the annotated manuscript sources. These suggestions are by no means exhaustive but are merely intended as starting points for future scholarship in selected areas in the history of twentieth-century American science.

Disciplinary Contours

The transformation of the life sciences in America in the twentieth century was shaped by earlier developments. Several areas of the biological sciences experienced significant growth during the second half of the nineteenth century. Museums of natural history, notably the Museum of Comparative Zoology in Boston, the Smithsonian Institution, Yale's Peabody Museum, and the American Museum of Natural History in New York City, fostered research and educational programs in botany, zoology, and paleontology. Marine biological laboratories, especially the one at Woods Hole, had grown by the beginning of the twentieth century into thriving scientific communities, where embryology and cytology flourished. The nation's agricultural research stations and agricultural colleges became active sites of applied and pure research in plant and animal breeding; attention to practical problems at coastal and lake fisheries contributed to the growth of embryology, ecology, and population biology. Diverse researches on animal nutrition and husbandry, plant and animal pathology, microbiology, and soil sciences developed during the late nineteenth century (albeit at different rates), under the auspices of the United States Department of Agriculture.[1]

The closing decades of the nineteenth century also saw the nascence of experimental biology, a biology curriculum based in liberal arts colleges and graduate schools, and independent from medical education. The champions of experimental biology, among them Thomas H. Morgan (at Bryn Mawr and Columbia), Edmund B. Wilson* (Columbia), Charles O. Whitman, Frank R. Lillie** and Jacques Loeb** (University of Chicago), H. Newell Martin (Johns Hopkins), and after 1920, William J. Crozier (Harvard), sought to break away from the intellectual traditions of natural history, descriptive zoology, botany, and vertebrate morphology. Imbued with the German research ideal, these American biologists, focusing on cytology and embryology, emphasized experimental evidence as a basis for explanations of life phenomena. The research laboratory became central to the scientific ethos of experimental biology.[2]

---

[1]J. Maienschein, "History of Biology," *Osiris* 1 (1985): 147–162; M. Rossiter, "The Organization of the Agricultural Sciences," in A. Oleson and J. Voss, eds., *The Organization of Knowledge in Modern America* (Baltimore: Johns Hopkins University Press, 1976), 211–248.

[2]G. Allen, *Life Science in the Twentieth Century* (New York: John Wiley and Sons, Inc., 1975), chapter 4; N. Reingold and I. Reingold, eds., *Science in America: A Documentary History, 1900-1939* (Chicago: University of Chicago Press, 1981), chapter 6; L. Owens, "Pure and Sound

Ironically, the integration of experimental biology into the academic curriculum was catalyzed through the medical connection, which biologists had sought to diminish. Motivated to a large extent by the reform of the medical curriculum, leading American universities had begun promoting in the late nineteenth century a core biological curriculum that included experimental embryology, cytology, and physiology, with the intention of upgrading medical training through fundamental biological knowledge. The commitment to scientific medicine also encouraged the development of physiological chemistry, the precursor of biochemistry. Although at the turn of the century departments of biology were still dominated by the older traditions of descriptive zoology and botany, new disciplinary trends had begun to emerge, and an institutional infrastructure—biology departments, professional societies, and journals—had been fairly well established.[3]

While some aspects which came to characterize the organization of biological knowledge in modern America were already in place early in this century, several distinctive features of the modern life sciences evolved in the following decades. The twentieth century, as several manuscript sources in this bibliography document, was shaped by its own political forces, social trends, and intellectual currents, resulting in the creation of uniquely American institutions of science which encouraged the development of new disciplines and research programs.

One of the new disciplines which emerged in the United States in the early decades of the twentieth century and is well documented in the APS collections was general physiology. In contrast to the old medically oriented physiology which focused primarily on structure and on specific tissues and organs, the new physiology emphasized quantitative explanations and fundamental mechanisms. It also stressed generality—the unity of biological phenomena in all organisms from protozoa to humans. As such, general physiology was partly a continuation of the split from the older descriptive morphological tradition, and in part a move away from clinical medicine.

The convoluted path of general physiology reflected uncertainty of disciplinary direction. In perennial struggle against colonization by medicine, general physiology represented more of a reaction than an active plan; by overlapping with biochemistry and biophysics, general physiology was vaguely defined, and did not have a coherent agenda. Non-medical general physiology was promoted by some of the champions of experimental biology, among them J. Loeb**, F.R. Lillie**, W.J.V. Osterhout*, and Simon

---

Government: Laboratories, Playing Fields, and Gymnasia in the Nineteenth Century Search for Order," *Isis* 76 (1985): 182–194.

[3]R.E. Kohler, *From Medical Chemistry to Biochemistry* (Cambridge: Cambridge University Press, 1982), chapter 7; P. Pauly, "The Appearance of Academic Biology in Late-Nineteenth Century America," *Journal of the History of Biology* 17 (1984): 369–397.

Flexner*; aspects of their scientific activities are documented in the manuscript sources at the APS.[4]

Perhaps the greatest influence of all was exerted by Simon Flexner*, who had made his mark in bacteriology and pathology before the turn of the century; the extensive collection of his papers at the APS provides a wealth of information on his scientific contributions. As director of the Rockefeller Institute for over thirty years, he was responsible for bringing in Loeb**, Osterhout*, Levene**, Northrop**, Wendell M. Stanley**, Thomas M. Rivers*, Peyton Rous*, Donald D. Van Slyke**, and Ralph W.G. Wyckoff**. As chief editor of the *Journal of Experimental Medicine*, as trustee of major foundations that promoted the life sciences, and in his advisory role for numerous organizations, Flexner played a pivotal role in shaping experimental biology, general physiology, biophysics, and biochemistry in America.[5]

Given the variegated nature of general physiology (and the broadness of experimental biology), the visions of various practitioners gave rise to different research programs. Lillie's** work, for example, centered primarily on the physiology of fertilization, utilizing immunological and biochemical concepts of biological specificity. At the same time, as the manuscript sources show, he exercised strong influence on the development of experimental biology and general physiology through his departmental leadership at the University of Chicago, and through his powerful administrative contacts and wide-ranging scientific networks.[6]

The German émigré Jacques Loeb**, on the other hand, shunned administrative entanglements; his impact on general physiology was made primarily through his research and his charismatic personality. An arch-determinist, Loeb**, unlike Lillie**, approached physiology as a purely mechanistic process, completely reducible to the laws of physics and chemistry, and his investigations on fertilization and phototropism were aimed at the control of life. Like Lillie**, he promoted the idea that general physiology would best advance the life sciences when freed from its role of servant to medicine.[7]

Loeb's** ideas were closely shared by his protégé Osterhout*. Trained in a botanical tradition, Osterhout* utilized plant cells to study general vital phenomena such as membrane permeability, chemical composition and

[4]P. Pauly, "General Physiology and the Discipline of Physiology, 1890-1935," in G. Geison, ed., *Physiology in the American Context, 1850-1940* (Washington, D.C.: American Physiological Society, 1987), 195–207.

[5]G.W. Corner, *History of the Rockefeller Institute*, (New York: The Rockefeller Institute Press, 1964), passim; and "Simon Flexner," *Dictionary of Scientific Biography* (New York: Scribners, 1970-1980), 5: 39–41.

[6]For a good source on Lillie's scientific work and his institutional influence see K. Manning, *Black Apollo of Science* (New York: Oxford University Press, 1983).

[7]P. Pauly, *Controlling Life: Jacques Loeb and the Engineering Ideal in Biology* (New York: Oxford University Press, 1987).

electrolytic balance in cell fluids—highly quantitative studies which encompassed plant physiology, biochemistry, and biophysics. Beyond the laboratory, Osterhout* exerted influence on the growth of general physiology through his involvement and long-time co-editorship of the *Journal of General Physiology*, through publications aimed at a wide readership, and his leadership positions in professional societies.[8]

In contrast to the mechanistic reductive approach of Loeb** and his disciples (who also included John H. Northrop** of the Rockefeller Institute), the research school of W.B. Cannon* at Harvard's Laboratory of Experimental Physiology fostered an integrated approach to vital processes. His classic neurophysiological studies on the sympathetic nervous system, along with related studies of endocrine function, led him to coin the term "homeostasis" to describe a self-regulating process by which the constancy of the internal environment is maintained. Although Cannon's* correspondence at the APS does not deal with his research, it does document his influence within the scientific establishment and his impact on experimental biology.[9]

Relative to experimental biology and general physiology, biochemistry (or physiological and biological chemistry, as it was called until the 1930s) was a late bloomer in the United States. Biochemistry (like physiology) received its greatest impetus within a medical context, and depended on the support of physiologists. Biochemistry, however, quickly surpassed physiology in status and resources. At the end of the nineteenth century only three departments—Russell H. Chittenden's** at Yale, Victor C. Vaughan's at the University of Michigan Medical School, and John J. Abel's at Johns Hopkins Medical School—offered research opportunities and courses in biochemistry. By 1910, the majority of medical schools had founded biochemistry programs and departments, and biochemists had established a disciplinary identity within professional societies and through the *Journal of Biological Chemistry*. By the 1920s, biochemistry was generally recognized as a discipline of primary importance and commanded abundant resources.[10]

The founders of American biochemistry were trained in Germany, where this subject was quite advanced during the second half of the nineteenth century. Their embryonic research programs tended to resemble those of their German mentors. Focusing mainly on basic composition of

[8]Osterhout's activities are discussed in G. Allen, *Thomas Hunt Morgan: The Man and His Science* (Princeton: Princeton University Press, 1979), chapters 6 and 7, and in Corner, *History of the Rockefeller Institute*, 176–177.

[9]Allen, *Life Sciences*, 95-103; S. Benison, *Walter B. Cannon: the Life and Times of a Young Scientist* (Cambridge: Harvard University Press, 1987); S.J. Cross and W.R. Albury, "Walter B. Cannon, L.J. Henderson, and the Organic Analogy," *Osiris* 3 (1987): 165–192.

[10]Kohler, *From Medical Chemistry to Biochemistry*, chapter 7; J. Fruton, *Molecules and Life* (New York: John Wiley and Sons, 1972), introduction; R.H. Chittenden, *The Development of Physiological Chemistry in the United States* (New York: Chemical Catalog Co., 1930).

substances in plants and animals—carbohydrates, proteins, enzymes—American biochemists emphasized blood chemistry, and chemical analyses of products involved in such metabolic processes as digestion and respiration. These early biochemical programs were influenced by the strong traditions of nutrition and agricultural chemistry in American universities. For example, at Yale, the work at the Connecticut Agricultural Experimental Station greatly influenced the development of protein chemistry under R.H. Chittenden**; his memoirs at the APS recount these early developments.

At the turn of the century, the impact of medical reform which swept through American universities not only accelerated the growth of biochemistry, but also inclined it toward a clinical service role. Until about 1940, biochemistry, except at those universities where the connection to agriculture and nutrition remained dominant (notably at the University of Wisconsin, where hundreds of biochemists were trained in food and drug research), developed principally in medical schools and was informed by concerns of physicians and medical physiologists. But even in the medical context, biochemistry underwent changes in the 1920s and 1930s, forging closer institutional ties and intellectual alliances with organic chemistry and physical chemistry. Increasingly, biochemists received their training in departments of chemistry, which were undergoing rapid growth after World War I. They applied new theories and laboratory techniques to study not only problems directly relevant to medicine, but also questions in theoretical biochemistry such as reaction kinetics, oxidation-reduction, and chemical structure.

As the papers of the influential biochemist William Mansfield Clark* show, from the 1920s to the mid-1950s he led at Johns Hopkins Medical School an elite research group that emphasized studies of equilibria and oxidation-reduction reactions in metabolic systems. Similarly, the growing influence of chemistry on biochemistry resulted in the appointment in 1928 of Hans T. Clarke* as head of the biochemistry department at Columbia's College of Physicians and Surgeons. His department, which focused on organic chemistry, and especially on the chemistry of proteins and steroids, became by 1940 one of the largest and most influential in biochemistry in America.[11]

Several research currents, notably enzymology and protein chemistry, shaped the direction of American biochemistry. During the 1920s and 1930s theories of enzyme kinetics were developed and hundreds of enzymes which catalyze diverse vital reactions were discovered, culminating in the early 1930s with the crystallization of several proteolytic enzymes. Manuscript sources at the APS on Nobel laureate John Howard Northrop**, who led

[11]Kohler, *From Medical Chemistry to Biochemistry*, chapter 10.

10

these researches at the Rockefeller Institute, include several files on his scientific activities.

The 1930s also saw the growing influence of the German organic chemist Emil Fischer on the development of protein chemistry in America. As his numerous students became directors of their own research programs, they emphasized Fischer's peptide theory of protein structure. Protein chemistry assumed a principal place within biochemistry, and the Rockefeller Institute, which had traditionally stressed a physico-chemical approach to biological knowledge, was in the vanguard of this field. In fact, this trend was in part responsible for the eclipse of nucleic acid research in the 1930s, since the primacy of proteins was regarded as the explanation to all phenomena involving biological specificity.[12] The manuscript sources on Phoebus A.T. Levene** and Max Bergmann* of the Rockefeller Institute contain materials on these trends in biochemistry. The Bergmann Papers* also document trends in leather chemistry, and through his extensive correspondence with biochemist Karl P. Link** of the University of Wisconsin, also developments in agricultural chemistry.

By the mid-1940s, due to the impact of gene research and the rise of molecular biology, the attention of biochemists was increasingly drawn to the biochemistry of nucleoproteins and nucleic acids, culminating in 1953 in the elucidation of the double helical structure of DNA, the genetic blue-print of life. This discovery, in turn, accelerated the shift away from protein research toward the biochemistry of nucleic acids. But in the 1930s and 1940s, only a few researchers were attracted to the study of the biological properties of nucleic acids. Geneticist Jack Schultz* at the California Institute of Technology was one of the early believers in the role of nucleic acids as hereditary determinants.

Schultz's* extensive correspondence with his close friend, Swedish biochemist Torbjörn O. Caspersson**, affords rare insights into the intellectual and social dynamics within the community of biochemists whose research interests were dominated by the protein paradigm. Similarly the papers of biochemist Erwin Chargaff* (in H.T. Clarke's* biochemistry department at Columbia), who had worked out in the 1940s a key element in the DNA puzzle, are an invaluable source on the intellectual and social challenges inherent in scientific work which is outside the mainstream of research.[13]

The differentiation between physiology and biochemistry has not resulted in a total intellectual separation between these disciplines. There has

[12]Fruton, *Molecules and Life*, chapter 3; R.C. Olby, *The Path to the Double Helix* (London: Macmillan Press, 1974), section 2.

[13]P. Abir-Am, "From Biochemistry to Molecular Biology: DNA and the Acculturated Journey of the Critic of Science Erwin Chargaff," *History and Philosophy of the Life Sciences* 2 (1980): 3–60.

been a wide common ground between the two areas, which in turn has accommodated within it other overlapping fields, specifically microbiology, immunology, and pathology. The close relations between physiology, pathology, and microbiology (especially bacteriology) developed during the late nineteenth century. With the acceptance of Pasteur's germ theory of disease and the rise of bacteriology, physiological processes in animals and plants could no longer be fully explained apart from microbiology—bacteriological knowledge then consisting mainly of microscopical classifications of bacteria based on morphology, differential staining, and life cycles. Following the medical reforms at the turn of the century, bacteriologists (trained mainly in Germany) had become central to the growth of life sciences. The discovery that submicroscopic filterable organisms called viruses cause diseases in plants and animals gave rise in the 1910s and 1920s to the new specialty of virology. Initially subsumed under bacteriology or microbiology, the study of viruses evolved by the 1940s into a major research area within molecular biology and cancer research.[14]

The papers of Simon Flexner* include extensive material on American microbiology in general, as well as on Flexner's* own contributions to the study of bacteria and viruses. The Library also houses the papers of microbiologists Peyton Rous*, Peter K. Olitsky*, and Thomas M. Rivers* of the Rockefeller Institute, scientists who had pioneered physiological investigations of animal and plant viruses. Rivers* and Rous* were especially instrumental in promoting virology through leadership of their respective departments, their key positions in professional societies and scientific journals, and their wide collegial networks.

In addition to its ties to the physiological and medical traditions, microbiology was also shaped by chemistry. In contrast to physiologists and microbiologists like Rous*, Olitsky*, and Rivers*, biochemists usually viewed bacteria as a bag of chemicals—especially enzymes—to be extracted, purified, characterized, and manipulated.[15] For example, biochemist Florence Siebert* spent her long career at the University of Pennsylvania (Phipps Institute) studying the chemical properties of the active principle in tubercle bacilli. As her papers illustrate, although she worked on clinical problems in a quasi-medical institution, she maintained strong intellectual and social bonds to the chemists' establishment that had shaped her career.

The scientific activities of Siebert*, as well as those of Rivers*, Rous*, and Olitsky*, also show that it is difficult to separate neatly the growth of microbiology (especially in the medical context) from the science of immu-

---

[14]S.M. Hughes, *The Virus: A History of the Concept* (New York: Science History Publications, 1977); L. Wilkinson, "The Development of the Virus Concept as Reflected in Corpora of Studies on Individual Pathogens," *Medical History* 23 (1979): 1–28.

[15]R.E. Kohler, "Innovation in Normal Science: Bacterial Physiology," *Isis* 76 (1985): 162-181.

nology. Indeed, with the acceptance of the germ theory of disease, the two fields had developed side by side; investigations of diseases of microbial origins paralleled studies of immunity. Serum therapies in the late nineteenth century gave way to searches for antibody-producing vaccines and therapeutic drugs of the twentieth century. Pharmaceutical research formed an important research area where microbiology, biochemistry, physiology, and immunology intersected intellectually, institutionally, and commercially.

As with the branched development of microbiology, immunology differentiated into cellular (or humoral) and chemical subspecialties. The cellular approach, exemplified by the research of Rous*, Rivers*, and Olitsky*, emphasized the role of immune cells (e.g., leucocytes, phagocytes, and macrophages) that defend the body against foreign invaders (antigens). Advocates of the physico-chemical approach to immunology, on the other hand, stressed the specificity of chemical reactions by which antibodies neutralize the effects of antigens, a research area known as immunochemistry or molecular immunology. Among the founders of immunochemistry were the Swedish Nobel laureate Svante Arrhenius**, and Austrian-born Karl Landsteiner* (discoverer of the four blood groups and their immunogenetic significance) of the Rockefeller Institute. While the Library's manuscript sources on these scientists do not deal directly with immunochemistry, they do offer interesting insights that help place each scientist's work within the social context which shaped his *Weltanschauung*.[16]

Biophysics, though a strong intellectual and technological force in the life sciences, was not only a late bloomer but also an anomalous field. The salient features of institutional infrastructure which serve as indicators of disciplinary growth—scientific societies, journals, departments, endowed chairs—have been largely absent in American biophysics. While in the second decade of the century there were influential research programs in biophysics in England (e.g., those of A.V. Hill and E.D. Adrian) and in Germany, biophysics research in America was just emerging.

Probably one of the barriers to the coalescence of biophysics as a discipline was its great diversity. A catch-all term for technical and theoretical applications of physics to biology, biophysics since the late nineteenth century encompassed investigations in muscle physiology, electrophysiology, acoustics, pneumatics, respiration, blood-flow, and cardio-vascular function. Biophysics utilized principles of optics and the laws of light propagation in microscopy, photosynthesis, and in studies of color vision. During the first two decades of the century, biophysics also came to include aspects of quantum theory and the interaction of radiation with biological matter:

[16]P. Mazumdar, "The Antigen-Antibody Reaction and the Physics and Chemistry of Life," *Bulletin of the History of Medicine* 48 (1974): 1–21; A.M. Silverstein, "History of Immunology," in W.E. Paul, ed., *Fundamentals of Immunology* (New York: Raven Press, 1984), 9–50.

applications of x-rays and ultraviolet rays to organisms and cells, radiation genetics, methods of x-ray diffraction for probing biomolecular structure, spectroscopy, the use of radioisotope tracers, and beginning in the 1950s, the techniques of nuclear magnetic resonance. With a primary emphasis on techniques and instruments and with specialized literature on a wide range of topics scattered in diverse scientific journals, biophysics remained an eclectic field that did not mature into a bona fide discipline until well into the 1950s.

In the 1920s, American biophysicists had begun carving out a small niche for themselves in the interstices between physics, engineering, biology, biochemistry, and physiology. Some of these early investigations (notably at the Universities of Michigan, Chicago, Wisconsin, Rochester, Pennsylvania, Columbia University, the Carnegie Institution of Washington, and the Rockefeller Institute) had begun to outline the scientific content of biophysics, initiating an awareness of its potential disciplinary autonomy. A new subdivision, formally designated as biophysics, first opened at the Rockefeller Institute in 1927 under Ralph W.G. Wyckoff**, who worked on the biological applications of x-ray crystallography and later on the design and construction of the ultracentrifuge. Although the division was terminated upon his departure in the late 1930s (and revived in the 1950s under the Institute's new director Detlev W. Bronk), Wyckoff's** embryonic research program, as the manuscript sources on Wyckoff** reveal, was very important for the growth of biophysics.[17]

It seems that by the late 1920s biophysics was "in the air," so to speak. In 1928 the new biology division at the California Institute of Technology under T.H. Morgan established a department of biophysics, and Hugo Fricke at the Biological Laboratory at Cold Spring Harbor founded a special laboratory of biophysics. That same year, the biophysics institute—the Eldridge Reeves Johnson Foundation—was founded at the University of Pennsylvania under the leadership of Detlev W. Bronk, the dean of American biophysics. A center for a wide range of studies in neurobiology and biophysics, the Johnson Foundation served as a nursery of the new field. Although the manuscript sources on Bronk are not substantial, minor correspondence with Bronk appears in many of the collections in this bibliography. Furthermore, the English biophysicist F.J.W. Roughton*—a specialist on hemoglobin and oxygen transport in the blood—had participated in projects at the Johnson Foundation. His correspondence and extensive scientific records document various aspects of biophysics not only at the University of Pennsylvania but in other institutions as well.[18]

[17]Corner, *History of the Rockefeller Institute*, 183–186.

[18]There is no single source for the history of biophysics although F. Brink Jr.'s article, "Detlev Wulf Bronk," in the *Memoirs of the National Academy of Science* 50 (1975): 3–40, provides a broad account of the growth of biophysics. I thank Bill Leslie for making material on the history of biophysics available to me.

These diverse activities did not coalesce into a discipline, however. As late as 1938 Warren Weaver, director of the Natural Sciences Division of the Rockefeller Foundation, observed that "biophysics...is still for the most part an orphan subject. Able young physicists, however genuine their interest, hesitate to devote themselves to a profession which is insufficiently recognized to offer a reasonable chance for a permanent job."[19]

The anomalous development of biophysics may well serve as a corrective to arguments of institutional determinism in the history of science. In spite of its lagging disciplinary status, biophysics had a major impact on the transformation of biology into a sophisticated technology-based science; these trends are reflected in a number of manuscript sources. Osterhout's* studies of membrane permeability and electrophysiology may be properly included in biophysics. In addition to the material on Ralph W.G. Wyckoff** and on F.J.W. Roughton*, the papers of Mildred Cohn* of the University of Pennsylvania contain accounts of various investigations in biophysics, especially the early applications of nuclear magnetic resonance to biological problems. The Roughton Papers* and the Cohn Papers* are enhanced by the material on Britton Chance**. The papers of Alexander Hollaender* (one of the founders of radiation genetics) provide a rich record on the growth of radiation genetics after World War II, and on the relation of that field to regulatory issues of environmental safety.

Patronage, Politics, and the Rise of Research

The intellectual developments in physiology, biochemistry, and biophysics (and related fields) were shaped by complex social factors, and influenced by national and global politics. These interrelated social and political forces shifted patterns of patronage of the life sciences, stimulated the rise of new research institutions (including industrial research laboratories), and especially through the two world wars led to a reorganization of scientific research and to an influx of émigré scientists to the United States. These trends in American science are represented in most of the manuscript sources in this bibliography.

The pattern of scientific patronage during the first five decades of this century may be roughly described as cyclical, having shifted from the public to the private sphere and back again. Early in the century, the life sciences—heavily weighted toward practical goals, especially agriculture—were sup-

---

[19]Quoted in R.E. Kohler, "The Management of Science: The Experience of Warren Weaver and the Rockefeller Foundation Programme in Molecular Biology," *Minerva* 14 (1976): 249–293.

ported mainly by the government. A wide range of biological investigations were conducted in the bureaus of the United States Department of Agriculture and in agricultural colleges. Some of these institutions (such as the University of Missouri and the University of Wisconsin) eventually became leading research centers in the life sciences; the manuscript sources on W.J. Robbins*, K.P. Link**, W.J.V. Osterhout*, W.M. Clark*, and P.K. Olitsky* document aspects of these developments. Agriculturally oriented science continued to be predominantly government science even in the following decades.

The state and federal governments also supported practically oriented research programs related to public health; the papers of E.L. Severinghaus* reflect aspects of these activities. But as the files in the Flexner Papers* on Wickliffe Rose and the Rockefeller Sanitary Commission show, public health causes, medically oriented projects, and bio-medical education were active domains of the large philanthropies, notably the various Rockefeller boards. With the creation of the Carnegie Corporation in 1911 and the Rockefeller Foundation in 1913, the support of the life sciences (with the exception of agriculture) increasingly came from the private sphere.[20]

Initially, before the 1920s, the Rockefeller and Carnegie foundations supported little research by individuals in universities. Having come into existence during the Progressive Era, the large foundations reflected the spirit of reform that permeated the first and second decades of this century. These reforms, manifested in major changes in public education, in the rise of various social movements, and in large-scale civic projects, were inspired in part by the growing influence of business, industry, and technology in American life, and were informed by a drive for efficiency and technical training. Science, previously occupying only a marginal place in American education, increasingly moved from the periphery to the center of the school curriculum.

Biology played an integral role in that transformation. Viewed as a means for effecting changes in society, the life sciences (and by extension the behavioral sciences) became the underpinnings of several social programs which received generous support from the large foundations. The support for eugenics and genetics research by the Carnegie philanthropies and Rockefeller's Bureau of Social Hygiene are examples par excellence of social reforms of the Progressive Era which were based on applied knowledge in the life sciences.[21] The APS library is a prime repository of archival sources on

[20]Reingold and Reingold, *Science in America*, chapter 6.

[21]B.D. Karl and S.N. Katz, "The American Private Philanthropic Foundations and the Public Sphere, 1890–1930," *Minerva* 19 (1981): 236–270; R.E. Calahan, *Education and the Cult of Efficiency* (Chicago: University of Chicago Press, 1962); D.N. Pickens, *Eugenics and the Progressives* (Nashville: Vanderbilt University Press, 1958).

eugenics; however, being an aspect of genetics, they are outside the scope of this bibliographic guide.

The emphasis by the Carnegie and Rockefeller foundations on large-scale projects of social utility did not preclude their supporting basic research (though not in a university context). During the first decade of the century, two major research institutes which had an enormous impact on the growth of the life sciences were established: the Carnegie Institution of Washington (1902) and the Rockefeller Institute for Medical Research (1901). Within the broad spectrum of its research activities (which included the physical, earth, and planetary sciences), the Carnegie Institution gave considerable support to biological research at its laboratories: the Department of Plant Biology (the Desert Laboratory), the Department of Marine Biology, the Nutrition Laboratory, the Department of Embryology, and the Department of Genetics (Station of Experimental Evolution) at Cold Spring Harbor.[22] The papers of Warren Harmon Lewis*, who worked at the Carnegie Institution, afford insights into activities at the Department of Embryology, and both the desert and marine laboratories.

Cold Spring Harbor* was enormously important for the growth of genetics, and Milislav Demerec*, its director after 1940, made it into a mecca for molecular biologists. It evolved into an international scientific center that promoted the cooperation of physicists, chemists, and biologists on fundamental problems in biology, biochemistry, and biophysics, with an emphasis on gene research. The papers of Milislav Demerec* and Jack Schultz*, as well as the Cold Spring Harbor* collection, document aspects of this transition from classical genetics to molecular biology.

In contrast to the Carnegie Institution of Washington, the Rockefeller Institute supported strictly biomedical research; clinical studies were conducted in the adjacent Institute Hospital. America's principal leaders of scientific medicine, the Johns Hopkins bacteriologist William H. Welch and his disciples ("Welch rabbits"), were a major force in planning the institute; the policies were implemented by Welch's protégé, Simon Flexner*, the Institute's director for over thirty years. Motivated by the gospel of scientific medicine, Flexner* and the Institute's leaders emphasized a physico-chemical approach to fundamental problems in physiology. While the German research ethos inspired individual freedom of inquiry, the Institute also encouraged interdisciplinary team research. In fact, the Rockefeller Institute became Adolph von Harnack's model of privately supported, project-oriented science when he founded the Kaiser-Wilhelm Institute in 1913.[23]

[22]N. Reingold, "National Policy in Private Foundations: The Carnegie Institution of Washington," in Oleson and Voss, *The Organization of Knowledge*, 313–341.

[23]Corner, *History of the Rockefeller Foundation*; R. Dubos, *The Professor, the Institute, and DNA* (New York: Rockefeller University Press, 1976); F. Ringer, "The German Academic Community," in Oleson and Voss, *The Organization of Knowledge*, 409–429.

Beginning in 1906 with three departments—Pathology and Bacteriology, Physiology and Pharmacology, and Chemistry—the Institute by the 1930s had expanded into four laboratory buildings. Even in the Institute's Hospital, approximately half of the space was designed primarily for laboratories, reflecting the primacy of research. The Institute's laboratories created in the 1920s included physical chemistry, photobiology, biophysics, cytology, and endocrinology. The Institute's Princeton branch—the Department of Animal and Plant Pathology—became by the late 1930s a world-class center of biochemistry and microbiology, where J.H. Northrop** and W.M. Stanley** conducted their Nobel Prize-winning work on proteins.[24]

Aside from the emphasis on theoretical physico-chemical aspects of vital phenomena, the Rockefeller Institute was in the vanguard of laboratory technology. The Institute's workshops produced some of the most sophisticated instruments in the United States, including x-ray spectrographs, electrophoresis apparatus, and ultracentrifuges; some of the important innovations in chemical separation techniques of chromatography in the 1940s took place at the Institute. These various laboratory technologies became indispensable to the study of cells and molecules, and placed the Institute in the forefront of biomedical research. By the mid-1950s, the Rockefeller Institute (renamed The Rockefeller University) had become not only an international training center, but also a model for other departments and institutions in the life sciences.[25]

The manuscript sources at the Library are especially informative regarding this remarkably influential research institute. The voluminous collection of Simon Flexner's* papers, which documents the scientific and administrative activities at the Institute, is complemented by manuscript sources on biochemists, physiologists, microbiologists, and biophysicists. Taken together, the sources on Peyton Rous*, T.M. Rivers*, W.J.V. Osterhout*, Max Bergmann*, K. Landsteiner*, P.K. Olitsky*, R.W.G. Wyckoff**, P.A.T. Levene**, J.H. Northrop**, J. Loeb**, and W.M. Stanley** (and the papers at the APS of Florence R. Sabin, James B. Murphy, Eugene L. Opie, George W. Corner, and Rufus Cole) provide scholars with materials which cover a substantial portion of the history of the Rockefeller Institute.

The manuscript sources at the Library illuminate another important chapter in the history of the life sciences: the involvement of the United States in World War I, and the effect of the war on the subsequent direction of American science. On the technological and scientific level, cooperative war projects gave rise to new instruments and devices, to novel materials,

---

[24]L.E. Kay, "W.M. Stanley's Crystallization of the Tobacco Mosaic Virus," *Isis* 77 (1986): 450–472.

[25]The Rockefeller Institute became a model for the biology division of the California Institute of Technology planned in the late 1920s.

methods, and treatments. These developments, in turn, transformed the character of warfare and made science indispensable to it. On the social level, war activities were responsible for the emergence of a scientific community self-conscious of its importance to national welfare. World War I, sometimes referred to as the "chemists' war", was particularly important in the emergence of a strong academic and industrial chemistry. Led by a powerful scientific establishment, in which Simon Flexner played an important role, America's men of science played up the lessons of the war. Emphasizing the benefits of cooperative research and the need for new scientific institutions, they lobbied for a substantial increase in financial support for science from the private sector, especially the Carnegie and Rockefeller foundations.[26]

Historians of science have focused their attention on cooperative war projects which involved the physical sciences and engineering: submarine detection devices, aeronautic instrumentation, wireless communication, methods for computing projectile trajectories, atmospheric research, and projects of the Chemical Warfare Service. Relatively little, however, has been written on war-related projects in the life sciences. The Rockefeller Institute, for example, played an important role in these activities. Under the leadership of Simon Flexner*—Lieutenant Colonel and consultant on Army medical problems during the war—the chief task of the Institute was to conduct courses in bacteriology, clinical chemistry, and pathology for medical officers and technicians. Hundreds of army personnel were trained by the institute's staff, among them Olitsky* and Rous*. In addition to war-related medical training, Flexner's* laboratory developed a rapid method for producing serum to combat an outbreak of cerebrospinal meningitis, an antidysentery serum, and new techniques for typing and treating pneumonia. P.A.T. Levene's** laboratory was converted into a production site for pharmaceuticals such as barbitols and antidotes to mustard gas; in Loeb's** division J.H. Northrop** developed a microbial process for the production of acetone for explosives. Rous*, together with two colleagues at the Institute, developed methods for preserving human blood in blood banks, which facilitated blood transfusions.[27]

The manuscript sources on Flexner*, Olitsky*, and Rous* contain material on some of these war projects, affording glimpses into the early links between the life sciences and the military, ties which served as a precedent for the mobilization of life scientists during World War II. Complementing

[26]R.H. Kargon, ed., *The Maturing of American Science* (Washington, D.C.: American Association for the Advancement of Science, 1974), introduction; D.J. Kevles, "George Ellery Hale, the First World War, and the Advancement of Science in America," *Isis* 59 (1968): 427–437; A. Roland, "Science and War," *Osiris* 1 (1985): 247–272; D. Rhees, "The Chemists' Crusade: The Rise of an Industrial Science in Modern America, 1907-1922," Ph.D. dissertation, University of Pennsylvania, 1987.

[27]Corner, *History of the Rockefeller Institute*, chapter 6.

these sources on actual projects are the correspondence files between Oster-hout* and Arrhenius** and between J.T. Lloyd and Robbins*, which contain detailed accounts of Europe during the war years, the effects of the war on the international scientific community, and changing attitudes toward German science. These sources indicate that the involvement of the life scientists in the war was of greater significance than previously acknowledged.

As a result of the rising status of science during the war and the promotion of basic research as a national resource, science began to be supported on a massive scale by the large foundations. Beginning in 1919, the National Research Council—an institution established during the war—introduced a program of postdoctoral fellowships financed by the Rockefeller Foundation. During the 1920s, under the aegis of various boards, the Rockefeller philanthropies funneled millions of dollars into fellowship pro-grams and awarded multi-million dollar grants to science departments in universities. During the 1920s, the Rockefeller's General Education Board and International Education Board emphasized fundamental research in the physical sciences: physics, mathematics, and chemistry. Departments in the life sciences did receive grants-in-aid and young researchers were awarded Rockefeller Fellowships in biological fields, but these fields were not the first priorities.[28] As the Seibert Papers* show, the Guggenheim Foundation was an important source of funding for talented individuals in the life sciences.

Beginning in the 1930s, with the consolidation of the Rockfeller philanthropies, the Rockefeller Foundation reformulated its science policy, concentrating its resources on the biological sciences. Under the directorship of the former University of Wisconsin mathematical physicist Warren Weav-er, the Rockefeller Foundation's Natural Sciences Division allocated millions of dollars to grants and fellowships specifically aimed at developing a biology based on applications of physics and chemistry to fundamental problems of life. By circumventing institutional barriers and by crossing boundaries of traditional disciplines, Rockefeller grants and fellowships promoted coopera-tive projects which merged genetics, biochemistry, physiology, biophysics, microbiology, and immunology into the hybrid discipline of molecular biology.[29]

[28]S. Coben, "American Foundations as Patrons of Science: The Commitment to Individ-ual Research," in N. Reingold, ed., *The Sciences in the American Context: New Perspectives* (Washington, D.C.: Smithsonian Institution Press, 1979), 229–248.

[29]Kohler, "The Management of Science"; Kohler, "A Policy of the Advancement of Science: The Rockefeller Foundation, 1924–1929," *Minerva* 16 (1978): 480–515; P. Abir-Am, "The Discourse of Physical Power and Biological Knowledge in the 1930s: A Reappraisal of the Rockefeller Foundation's 'Policy' in Molecular Biology," *Social Studies of Science* 12 (1982), 341–362; E. Yoxen, "Giving Life a New Meaning: The Rise of the Molecular Biology Establishment," in N. Elias, H. Martins, and R. Whitly, eds., *Scientific Establishments and Hierarchies: Sociology of the Sciences* (Doerdrecht: D. Reidel Publishing Co., 1982), 4: 123–143; R. Fosdick, *The Story of the Rockefeller Foundation* (New York: Harper and Brothers, 1952).

In order to accomplish this massive reorganization of the life sciences, Weaver and his staff depended on the advice of experts—leaders in those branches of the life sciences relevant to the new program. Flexner*, of course, had a great deal of input into the "new biology" (about which he had several reservations), as did F.R. Lillie** and W.B. Cannon*. As the manuscript sources show, these men who had shaped the course of experimental biology at the turn of the century also influenced the design of the new biology in the 1930s. The papers of W.J. Robbins* are a highly informative source on the activities of the Rockefeller Foundation during its organizational phase of the early 1930s. Having traveled extensively in Europe and Asia, Robbins prepared detailed reports for the Foundation, describing numerous laboratories he had visited. These reports are not only a valuable source of information on the life sciences abroad, but also offer insights into the *modus operandi* of the Rockefeller Foundation during the 1930s. Bergmann's* correspondence with the Rockefeller Foundation illuminates the purposes and policy of its fellowship program.

The 1920s and 1930s also saw the rise of cooperation between the pharmaceutical industries and the universities. Sobered by the lessons of the war (particularly the dependence on German drugs), and with the abrogation of German-owned patents in 1917, American drug companies came to regard biochemical research as an essential resource for the maintenance of a competitive edge, both in wartime and peacetime. Several pharmaceutical houses in the 1920s courted researchers in physiology, biochemistry, pharmacology, and microbiology; they established consultantships and industrial fellowships, and cultivated joint projects with university departments. Particularly strong links among academic biochemistry, pharmacology, and nutrition developed in the 1920s between the University of Wisconsin and a number of food and drug industries; Elmer L. Severinghaus* played an active role in that liaison.[30]

Due partly to industry's growing emphasis on research, and partly to the war's lessons, America's custodians of "pure *Wissenschaft*", who previously had looked askance at utilitarian science, entered increasingly into industrial research. A new breed of life scientists emerged, among them A.N. Richards of the University of Pennsylvania and Merck & Company, Roger Adams of the University of Illinois and Abbot Laboratories, A.L. Tatum of the University of Wisconsin and Parke-Davis, all of whom forged early links between academic life sciences and pharmaceutical houses. Eli Lilly and Co., for example, began its cooperative relations with academia by sponsoring a few projects in Woods Hole in the 1920s; by the 1940s it had developed in-house research facilities as well as an elaborate system of contracts with

[30]J. Swann, "The Emergence of Cooperative Research Between American Universities and the Pharmaceutical Industry, 1920-1940," Ph.D. dissertation, University of Wisconsin, 1985.

biochemists and physiologists. Some of the collaborations of Lilly (and other pharmaceutical companies) are documented in the Seibert Papers*, the Chargaff Papers*, and the Neuberg Papers*. Hoffmann-La Roche, having established sophisticated in-house research in the 1930s, was able to attract Severinghaus* to become its director of research in the 1940s. Several letters in the Severinghaus Papers* afford interesting insights into issues concerning industry-university relations in the life sciences.

The Impact of World War II

The life sciences in the 1930s were also greatly influenced by the political events in Europe, forces that culminated in the eruption of World War II. With the rise of the Nazi Party in Germany and the growing virulence of anti-Semitism, the academic futures of Jewish scientists in Germany became bleak. Prominent researchers at universities and the Kaiser-Wilhelm Institutes were relieved of their posts, and the careers of young scientists of Jewish descent were truncated. Many deposed scholars from the physical, biological, and social sciences made their way to America. With the support of the Rockefeller Foundation, and through special funds and committees established to help refugee scholars, these European scientists found academic posts and research opportunities in the United States.[31]

The intellectual migration of the 1930s had important consequences for the development of the life sciences, especially biochemistry and molecular biology in the 1940s and 1950s. Austrian biochemist Erwin Chargaff*, who developed his program under H.T. Clarke* at Columbia, made some of the most significant contributions to nucleic acids research in the late 1940s, work which led to the elucidation of the structure of DNA. A vociferous critic of American culture, Chargaff* maintained strong professional and emotional bonds with European colleagues; his correspondence offers cross-cultural perspectives on the intellectual and institutional aspects of biochemistry research. In contrast to Chargaff*, Max Bergmann* adopted his new homeland with great enthusiasm. His research program in protein chemistry at the Rockefeller Institute was extremely influential, and as his correspondence reveals, he helped several German biochemists to emigrate to America. Among these deposed scholars was Carl Neuberg*, former director of the

---

[31]D. Fleming and B. Bailyn, eds., *The Intellectual Migration: Europe and America, 1930-1960* (Cambridge: Harvard University Press, 1969); J.C. Jackman and C.M. Borden, eds., *The Muses Flee Hitler: Cultural Transfer and Adaptation, 1930–1945* (Washington, D.C.: Smithsonian Institution Press, 1983).

Kaiser-Wilhelm Institute for Biochemistry, and a leader in carbohydrate chemistry. The Neuberg Papers* contain extensive correspondence with prominent scientists in Germany, documenting a sadder and less successful story of an intellectual migration.

The political events of the 1930s that precipitated the exodus of German scientists eventually drew America into the war in 1941. During the "preparedness" phase (1940-1941), the leaders of American science reorganized the nation's scientific resources for the demands of war. The Office of Scientific Research and Development (OSRD) was established under the leadership of Vannevar Bush, Director of the Carnegie Institution of Washington, for the purpose of contracting with educational institutions, scientific organizations, individuals, and industries in order to coordinate war-related research. Within the OSRD, the Committee on Medical Research (CMR) was assembled under the leadership of the University of Pennsylvania pharmacologist Alfred N. Richards to develop war projects in the life sciences.[32]

The organization of divisions and projects during World War II was far more orderly and efficient than during World War I. A subcommittee on medicine dealt with problems such as infectious and tropical diseases and aviation medicine. The papers of F.J.W. Roughton*, an expert on blood-oxygen and high-altitude physiology, document some of his war activities in the United States. In addition to CMR projects, work related to diseases was conducted within the Army's and Navy's Medical Corps. A team of researchers at the Rockefeller Institute—the "Naval Research Unit"—under the direction of (Captain) T.M. Rivers*, worked on projects such as epidemic diseases, bacterial and viral research, immunology, and typing of pneumonia; the Rivers Papers* contain several files about these war-time projects.[33]

Research in physiology within the OSRD included the development of blood substitutes and agents for boosting resistance to disease. The blood-fractionation project at Edwin J. Cohn's** biochemistry laboratory at Harvard (described in the Joseph Stokes, Jr. Papers at the APS) was a principal achievement of CMR. Most biochemists worked on the production of hormones, penicillin, drugs, and bio-organic war chemicals, projects which were frequently coordinated with pharmaceutical firms. In fact, an important by-product of the war effort was an even closer tie between the drug industries and academic research in the life sciences. The Chargaff Papers* contain several files on biochemistry work within the OSRD, as well as on the subsequent ties of his research to the food and drug industries.

[32]G.W. Gray, *Science at War* (New York: Harper and Brothers, 1943); J.P. Baxter III, *Scientists Against Time* (New York: Little and Brown, 1946); I. Stewart, *Organizing Scientific Research for War* (Boston: Little and Brown, 1948); Roland, "Science and War," 263–267.

[33]Corner, *History of the Rockefeller Institute*, chapter 20; S. Benison, *Tom Rivers: Reflection on a Life in Medicine and Science, An Oral Memoir* (Cambridge: M.I.T. Press, 1967).

At the end of World War II (which, in spite of the life scientists' contributions, is sometimes referred to as the "physicists' war") science emerged even more triumphant than in the previous war. Massive war research such as the Manhattan Project, the development of the proximity fuse, and the penicillin and blood-fractionation projects forged strong links between science and government, bonds that could not be readily severed. Scientists learned what could be accomplished with the large-scale combinations of basic research and rapid development of its applied technologies. The OSRD was disbanded in 1945, but leaders of American science played up the "lessons of the bomb" and lobbied for the support of "big science" by the federal government. Not everyone embraced the wartime model during peacetime. The proponents of free enterprise, especially the Rockefeller and Carnegie foundations, opposed the concept of "planned" research. After a few years of public debate over the patronage of science, the convoluted path to federally supported science culminated in 1950 with the creation of the National Science Foundation.[34]

Although the life sciences within the OSRD were not as visible in the war effort as some of the large-scale projects in the physical sciences, researchers in the biological sciences were quite conscious of their contributions, as well as of their relative lack of recognition and prestige. They launched a vigorous campaign to secure for themselves a stable institutional position within the new federally funded science. The founding of the American Institute of Biological Sciences (AIBS) in 1947, and the substantial expansion of the National Institutes of Health (NIH) were the outcomes of these efforts. Little has been written about the AIBS, which by the mid-1960s experienced serious problems with its finances and reputation; the AIBS files in the papers of W.H. Lewis*, P. Rous*, and J. Schultz* help illuminate this little-known episode in the history of the life sciences. The papers of plant physiologist W.J. Robbins*, a central figure in the coordination of postwar science, are a rich source on the strengthening of biology in the postwar era.[35]

The National Institutes of Health, which supported the researches of several scientists included in this bibliography, has remained the single most important federal institution in the life sciences, in terms of policy-making, regulatory functions, peer review, and the allocation of research funds.[36]

[34]D.J. Kevles, "The National Science Foundation and the Debate over Postwar Research Policy, 1942–1945," *Isis* 68 (1977): 18. These issues are also discussed in D. Noble, *Forces of Production* (New York: Alfred E. Knopf, 1984): 2–20, and N. Reingold, "Vannevar Bush's New Deal for Research: or The Triumph of the Old Order," *Historical Studies in the Physical Sciences* 17 (1987): 299–344.

[35]Daniel S. Greenberg, "American Institute of Biological Sciences," *Science* 139 (1963), 319.

[36]For the pre-World War II antecedents see V. A. Harden, *Inventing the NIH: Federal Biochemical Research Policy, 1887-1937* (Baltimore: Johns Hopkins University Press, 1986).

Having come a full cycle, the life sciences evolved from being mainly government-sponsored early in this century, to being supported primarily by the private sector during the interwar period, and back to federally funded research during the postwar era, except on a radically larger scale. The probing of cells and molecules now entailed sophisticated apparatus and team-work, inflating annual institutional budgets to millions of dollars.

The intensified financial commitment mirrored the rising academic status of biology. By 1960 the life sciences had entered an era often referred to as a "golden age". Two major problems had been solved in the early 1950s: the structure of proteins, and the structure of nucleic acids, issues that have been generally regarded as essential to explaining and controlling most vital phenomena on the molecular and cellular levels. Under the new lens of molecular biology, the physico-chemical study of microorganisms had been intensified, molecular immunology had come to dominate the approach to the immune system, cancer research had emerged as a major federal goal, and neurophysiology, especially brain research, became a new frontier. American universities and scientific institutes not only played a leading role in many of these researches, but also attracted scientists from abroad; in a sense an attenuated form of the intellectual migration continued well past the war period.

While World War II was indeed a major turning point in the development of several fields in the life sciences—notably molecular and cellular biology—the transformations had begun at the turn of the century. Physiology, biochemistry, and to some extent biophysics were nurtured within the crusade of scientific medicine. World War I pointed up the need for biomedical research, for promoting physiology, biochemistry, and pharmacology as national resources, which in turn resulted in a commitment by the private sector to a large-scale support of research. The policy of the Rockefeller Foundation to concentrate massive funds in a physico-chemical attack on cells and molecules created a hybrid discipline—molecular biology—that altered the intellectual and social character of biological research. The manuscript sources annotated in Part Two document major episodes within that transformation. Not all aspects of the history of the life sciences are equally well represented in this bibliography. However, taken together, these records form an important resource in mapping some of the prominent intellectual and social contours of the life sciences over a period of half a century.

1. Life Science in the Agricultural Context

As mentioned earlier, major areas in the life sciences were nurtured within the intellectual traditions of agriculture and nutrition. As a result of the passage of the Morrill Land-Grant Act (1862), the Hatch Act (1887), and the Adams Act (1906), research in agricultural colleges and experiment stations flourished. With the sharp rise in the budget of the United States Department of Agriculture (USDA) at the turn of the century, the number of agricultural scientists increased greatly. Sizable research programs in plant physiology and biochemistry, in entomology, soil microbiology and chemistry, and in biochemical nutrition developed in agricultural schools in the 1910s, reflecting the rapid growth of agricultural science. Some of these investigations also became important in biomedical research.

Yet the history of twentieth-century agricultural sciences has not received attention commensurate with its importance. Historians have traced the development of biochemistry and physiology mainly within a medical context, and the handful of studies on agricultural science focus on the late nineteenth and early twentieth centuries.[37] This lacuna may be partially filled by the examining the manuscript sources on W.J.V. Osterhout*, P.K. Olitsky*, W.J. Robbins*, and K.P. Link**.

The Osterhout Papers* (1894–1961) provide a valuable record of a career which began at the botany department of Brown University, continued at the botany departments of the University of California at Berkeley and Harvard, culminating in Osterhout's* tenure as head of the physiology department at the Rockefeller Institute for Medical Research. His physico-chemical studies utilized plant cells for probing basic physiological phenomena such as permeability and bio-electric potentials, thus linking the agricultural and medical traditions in intellectual content, as well as in institutional context. The overlap between medical and agricultural concerns is also highlighted in the Olitsky Papers*, which contain materials on his work in

---

[37]For example, R.E. Kohler, *From Medical Chemistry to Biochemistry*; M. Rossiter, "The Organization of the Agricultural Sciences," in Oleson and Voss, *The Organization of Knowledge*, 211–248; C.E. Rosenberg, *No Other Gods* (Baltimore: Johns Hopkins University Press, 1976), part II. Two recent correctives are: D.K. Fitzgerald, "The Business of Breeding: Public and Private Development of Hybrid Corn in Illinois, 1890–1940," Ph.D. dissertation, University of Pennsylvania, 1985, and B.N. Kimmelman, "A Progressive Era Discipline: Genetics at American Agricultural Colleges and Experimental Stations, 1900–1920," Ph.D. dissertation, University of Pennsylvania, 1987.

microbiology for the USDA in relation to the hoof-and-mouth disease outbreak.

The Robbins Papers* (1890–1978), on the other hand, reflect a long career strictly within the botanical and agricultural context. These papers contain a wealth of information on scientific and administrative aspects of agriculturally oriented research programs (mainly plant physiology). These include programs in several major American and European universities, at agricultural colleges and experimental stations, and at the USDA.

The Link** correspondence (6 files, 1930–1945) in the Bergmann Papers* covers a substantial part of Link's career in agricultural chemistry at the University of Wisconsin. His program, which addressed a wide range of topics in nutritional biochemistry and carbohydrate chemistry, was one of America's most influential research schools in biochemistry in terms of scientific discoveries as well as in training many students. Although these manuscript sources document only a fraction of the story of agricultural chemistry, they are valuable material as case studies and provide insights into the complexity of the larger picture.

2. Academic Biochemistry and Commercial Concerns

The food and drug industries played a central role in the growth of biochemistry during the interwar period. During these years the major pharmaceutical houses, among them Eli Lilly, Hoffmann-La Roche, Merck and Co., and Parke-Davis established cooperative research with departments of biochemistry and physiology in major universities, projects which were administered through elaborate systems of contracts and industrial research fellowships. These bonds were further strengthened during World War II, when most academic biochemists worked in collaboration with the pharmaceutical industries on war projects sponsored by the OSRD. By the 1950s industrial and academic research in biochemistry was inextricably linked.

Scholars have begun examining this powerful scientific symbiosis, but more needs to be done in order to understand how commercial goals meshed or conflicted with academic research, especially in the postwar period.[38] One can gain some insights into issues surrounding industry-university relations from the papers of the Wisconsin biochemist E. Severinghaus* (1920–1945),

[38]Two recent examples are J. Liebenau, "Medical Science and Medical Industry, 1890–1929: A Study of Pharmaceutical Manufacturing in Philadelphia," Ph.D. dissertation, University of Pennsylvania, 1981, and J. Swann, "The Emergence of Cooperative Research Between American Universities and the Pharmaceutical Industry, 1920–1940," Ph.D. dissertation, University of Wisconsin, 1985.

who became director of research at Hoffmann-La Roche in 1945. The Seibert Papers* (1920–1970s) contain about twenty files (1930s–1960s) on her cooperation with several commercial concerns. Similarly, the Chargaff Papers* (1931–1971) contain correspondence on his links with Hoffmann-La Roche, Bio-vin, Upjohn, Eli Lilly, Rohm and Haas, and Parke-Davis. Biochemical research was integral to the growth of other industries. The ties between the fermentation industries and academic research are seen in the files in the Neuberg Papers* (1929–1956), and also in the records on the leather industry in the Bergmann Papers* (1930–1945).

3. *Life Science and War*

Science, technology, and the military have been linked for centuries; during the two world wars these bonds were greatly strengthened. After World War I scientific research and its applications came to be regarded as national resources, imparting power and prestige to a newly emerged scientific establishment. The men involved also masterminded the reorganization of scientific research and development during World War II. Some aspects of that reorganization have become permanent features of American science.

In contrast to their counterparts in the physical sciences, cooperative war projects in the life sciences have been largely ignored and their long-term impact on the organization of research remains unexplored. This important chapter in the history of science may be broached by utilizing several manuscript sources which contain material on the cooperation of life scientists with the military.

The Chargaff Papers* (1931–1971) contain files on his OSRD projects, which include material on the chemistry of blood coagulants. There is abundant information in the Rivers Papers* (1941–1963) on biomedical research and the Navy, and on the Armed Forces Epidemiological Board. There is extensive documentation in the Rous Papers* (1917–1970) on the development of procedures for preserving blood in blood banks, and in the Olitsky Papers* (1917–1964) on his work in microbiology. The manuscript sources on E.J. Cohn** include records related to his large-scale project of blood fractionation. The Roughton Papers* (1920–1960) contain correspondence on his war research in the context of aviation medicine, and the Robbins Papers* contain materials on life science during World War I and World War II, and important records on the global impact of American science in the decade after World War II.

The emerging interdependence between life science, the government, and the military in the early postwar era is also documented in the Neuberg

Papers* (1929–1956), through his various projects for the Atomic Energy Commission and the Office of Naval Research; the Hollaender Papers* (1950–1970) contain materials on the links between the Atomic Energy Commission and the development of radiation genetics. Taken together, the manuscript sources on life science and the military are a valuable resource for mapping out aspects of this important connection from the 1910s well into the 1950s.

4. *Women in Science*

With the trend toward a social history of science, there has been a growing interest in the role of women in science and in the relations between gender and science.[39] As scholars who have ventured into that field attest, the paucity of materials or inaccessibility of sources have hindered those interested in the careers of women in science. Only a handful of women during the first half of this century have attained the kind of prominence that results in abundant biographical records; few have been sufficiently connected within their disciplines to leave copious professional correspondence. It is therefore fortunate when rich sources on women in science are available, and it is important that these be utilized in order to gain a greater understanding of both women's contributions to science and the social dynamics of their interactions with colleagues.

The Florence Seibert Papers* (1920–1970s) contain a wealth of information on her long career as a biochemist, from her undergraduate training through her first phase in tuberculosis research, and her second phase in cancer research. Having attained international recognition, Seibert* left abundant correspondence with male and female colleagues, biographical material, and an autobiography. These records are a valuable resource on women in science. The APS Library also houses the papers of Florence R. Sabin, a prominent biomedical researcher, the only woman Member of the Rockefeller Institute, and the first woman to be elected to the National Academy of Science (1925). Studies based on the Sabin Papers (supplemented by several files on Sabin in the Flexner Papers*) promise to enrich greatly our knowledge of women in science.

[39]Recent scholarship includes E. Fox-Keller, *A Feeling for the Organism: The Life and Work of Barbara McClintock* (New York: W.H. Freeman and Co., 1983); idem, *Reflections on Gender and Science* (New Haven: Yale University Press, 1985); M. Rossiter, *Women Scientists in America: Struggles and Strategies to 1940* (Baltimore: Johns Hopkins University Press, 1982); P. Abir-Am and D. Outram eds., *Uneasy Careers and Intimate Lives: Women in Science, 1789–1979* (New Brunswick: Rutgers University Press, 1987).

5. Networks, Peer Reviews, and Scientific Research

The growth of the social studies of science in the 1960s and 1970s has focused attention on social constellations such as scientific networks, invisible colleges, collaborative teams, coauthorships, and the peer review process.[40] How are scientific studies judged, who judges, and how is science validated through the major journals? These are some fruitful inquiries that promise to bring new insights into the processes by which scientific research becomes legitimized, and mainstream science defined. The process of peer review for publications in scientific journals, for example, encompasses important aspects of scientific networks and research collaborations, forming a natural locus where social and intellectual factors intersect.

The Rous Papers* (1917–1970) afford a unique opportunity to explore the publication process in several areas in the life sciences through a close examination of hundreds of files on the *Journal of Experimental Medicine*, of which Rous* was an editor for fifty years. These files contain submissions, lists of reviewers, referee responses, rebuttals, and correspondence related to publications and editorial policies. It is a valuable source of insights into the complex social and intellectual web of science, encompassing physiology, biochemistry, biophysics, microbiology, and immunology. It also reveals trends in the evolution of the life sciences over a period of nearly half a century.

6. The Rise of Cancer Research

The problem of cancer had been viewed as a murky research area already at the turn of the century, a risky project for a young scientist. "Whatever you do, don't commit yourself to the cancer problem", was W.H. Welch's advice to his protégé Peyton Rous*, who was about join the Rockefeller Institute in 1909.[41] Within a few weeks Rous* made a series of discoveries which led him to conclude that viruses cause cancer in chickens. His work established the field of tumor virology and revolutionized cancer research. Because of a prolonged resistance by the medical profession, Rous's* research was not

---

[40]See, for example, D. de S. Price and D. Beaver, "Collaboration in an Invisible College," *American Psychologist* 21 (1966): 1011–1018; D. Crane, *Invisible Colleges: Diffusion of Knowledge in Scientific Communities* (Chicago: University of Chicago Press, 1972); N.C. Mullins, *Social Networks among Biological Scientists* (New York: Arno Press, 1980); N. Reingold, "On Not Doing the Papers of Great Scientists," *British Journal of History of Science* 20 (1987): 29–38.

[41]Corner, *History of the Rockefeller Institute*, 109–110.

followed up until the 1930s. He was awarded the Nobel Prize fifty-six years after his discovery.

The late 1930s were a watershed in cancer research. Through a series of congressional measures aimed at controlling cancer and promoting cancer research, the National Cancer Institute came into being and rising budgets began attracting life scientists to the field in greater numbers. In the late 1940s a new force spurred the expansion of cancer research through the financial and administrative contributions of Mary Lasker, leading to the organization of the American Cancer Society.[42] By the 1960s, through private initiative and massive federal support, cancer research had evolved into a multi-million dollar enterprise, encompassing diverse areas of basic research and clinical practice.

The story of the rise of cancer research—intellectual trends and institutional imperatives—awaits writing, and the manuscript sources at the APS Library will be indispensable to the task.[43] The Rous Papers* (1917–1970) are by far the most comprehensive source, tracing the intellectual odyssey and institutional growth of his research program on cancer and viruses. The relationship of virology to cancer research is also reflected in the Rivers Papers* (1941–1963) and in the papers of J.B. Murphy, at the Library. There is a great deal about biochemistry and cancer research (1950s–1960s) in the Seibert Papers* and in the Neuberg Papers* (1929–1956); and a wealth of scientific information and correspondence on cytology and cancer research in the Lewis Papers* (1913–1964). The connection between genetics, mutagenic effects, cytogenetics, and problems related to cancer research are documented in the Schultz Papers* (1920–1971), the Hollaender Papers* (1950–1970), and in the Abramson files and Cancer Research Project files of the Demerec Papers* (1917–1966).

7. The Polio Vaccine: Scientific Truths and Political Realities

The story of polio research, which culminated in 1952 in the development of the Salk vaccine and a mass-immunization program, is one of the most dramatic and instructive episodes in the history of biomedical research.

[42]P. Starr, *The Social Transformation of American Medicine* (New York: Basic Books, Inc., 1982), 340–343.

[43]Steps in this direction are: I. Berenblum, *Man Against Cancer: The Story of Cancer Research* (Baltimore: The Johns Hopkins University Press, 1952), and J. Patterson, *The Dread Disease: Cancer and Modern American Culture* (Cambridge: Harvard University Press, 1987).

Spanning a period of about three decades (1928–1958), the researches surrounding the development of the Salk vaccine ranged over a broad scientific spectrum: virology, biochemistry, immunology, public health, and drug manufacturing. It was also an instance in which public debate and political imperatives were intertwined with longstanding scientific controversies over the safety and effectiveness of different polio vaccines.

Since 1928, when it was firmly established that poliomyelitis is caused by a virus, the search for a polio vaccine had led to emotionally charged debates about the use of attenuated live-virus vaccines and vaccines made of the killed virus. Among those involved in the debates were researchers at the Rockefeller Institute, including Simon Flexner*, P.K. Olitsky*, A. Sabin, and T.M. Rivers**. By the time Jonas Salk began his polio research at the University of Pittsburgh in the 1940s, the National Foundation for Infantile Paralysis (established by Franklin D. Roosevelt in 1937) had launched a multi-million dollar campaign against the dreaded affliction. Headed by Basil O'Connor, the National Foundation coordinated all aspects of the polio program from basic research to public relations, with Rivers playing a central role, especially after retiring from his directorship of the Institute's hospital in 1955.

Some parts of the story of polio research and the development of the vaccine have been told.[44] However, there is no complete study which ties together the various intellectual and social aspects of the polio research program, from the laboratory bench to field trials, from academic debate to congressional hearings. Such a study promises to reveal a great deal not only about the histories of virology and immunology, but also about the institutional contexts which shaped different research approaches to the polio problem and about the interaction between science and the public. The Rivers Papers* (1941–1963) contain numerous files on the National Foundation and polio research, as well as several correspondence files with A. Sabin (the proponent of the live-virus vaccine), and J. Salk (the developer of the killed-virus vaccine). There are several correspondence files on A. Sabin in the Rous Papers* (including files in the *Journal for Experimental Medicine*), and significant material related to polio research in the Olitsky Papers*. These manuscript sources do not document the entire story, but they do provide material for important aspects of it.

[44]Benison, *Tom Rivers*; Corner, *History of the Rockefeller Institute*; a popular account by G. Williams, *Virus Hunters* (New York: Alfred A. Knopf, 1960); N. Rogers, "Screen the Baby Swat the Fly: Polio in the Northeastern United States, 1916," Ph.D. dissertation, University of Pennsylvania, 1986.

PART TWO

Annotated Entries

Primary Group: Manuscript Collections

1. Bergmann, Max (1884–1944). Biochemist.
   Papers, ca. 1930–1945, ca. 7500 items (7 1/2 ln.ft.).

Max Bergmann, formerly director of the Kaiser-Wilhelm Institute for Leather Research, joined the Rockefeller Institute in 1933; he was one of many German scientists of the intellectual migration. A protégé of Emil Fischer, Bergmann had developed in Germany a leading center for protein chemistry, attracting students from around the world. His successful career continued in his new homeland, which he considered "the best country on the globe" (Felix Haurowitz file, 8 July 1943). His research program, which focused on the action of proteolytic enzymes on synthetic peptides and on the problem of protein structure, aimed at explaining the biological specificity of proteins. As determinants of specificity, proteins were then generally regarded as the active hereditary material in the chromosomes; Bergmann's investigations were also intended to account for this genetic specificity. The Bergmann Papers—letters, reports, addresses, and lectures—are therefore important not only for the history of biochemistry, but also for the history of molecular genetics.

The correspondence shows Bergmann to be a central figure within the international network of protein chemists, and instrumental in helping other émigré biochemists in the 1930s. The letters also document the importance of Bergmann's laboratory as a training center; among his young assistants were Stanford Moore and William H. Stein, who developed sensitive techniques of chromatography. In addition to basic work on proteins, Bergmann remained associated with leather research, and the collection contains material on this link between academic biochemistry and commercial leather research in America.

The correspondence files include: The American Chemical Society (ca. 1930s–1940s), including materials on symposia on nutrition; American Leather Chemists Association (ca. 1930s–1940s); W.T. Astbury (late 1930s), correspondence regarding Bergmann's theories of protein structure; R. Ballentine (2 files, 1930s–1940s), scientific and professional communications; E. Chargaff* (ca. 1940s), professional exchanges; A. Chibnall (1930s–1940s), on professional activities related to protein chemistry; W.M. Clark* (1942), on technical issues in protein chemistry; H.T. Clarke* (2 files, 1930s–1940s), including materials on the network of protein chemists; M. Demerec* (ca. 1940), on the 1941 Cold Spring Harbor Symposium; V. Du Vigneaud** (ca. 1930s–1940s) on scientific and social matters; A. Einstein, personal matters; H.O.L. Fischer (3 files, ca. 1930s–1940s), on scientific and social concerns; Simon Flexner* (ca. 1930s), Flexner's reaction to Bergmann's work; H. Fraenkel-Conrat (2 files, ca. 1930s–1940s), important correspondence regarding Fraenkel-Conrat's career as an émigré life scientist; J. Fruton (3 files, ca. 1930s–1940s), on professional and scientific matters; H. Gasser (2 files, ca. 1930s–1940s), technical correspondence and response to W. Stein's work; F.B. Hanson (ca. 1930s), informative correspondence about Rockefeller Foundation Fellowships, including the fellowship of C. Niemann; F. Haurowitz (1943), regarding Haurowitz's immigration to the United States; Institute for Leather Research (ca. 1930s–1940s), informative material about organic chemistry of leather and tanning; American Leather Chemists Association (ca. 1930s–1940s), on Bergmann's dealings with administrative and social aspects within the profession; P.A.T. Levene** (ca. 1930s), including Levene's reaction to Bergmann's research and materials related to the establishment of the Protein Committee; K. Link** (6 files, 1930s–1940s), about various aspects of biochemistry, especially agricultural chemistry in Wisconsin; O. Meyerhoff (ca. 1940s), on Meyerhoff's move to the University of Pennsylvania; H.J. Muller (ca. 1930s), in regard to an invitation to participate in the Seventh International Congress of Genetics; C. Neuberg* (ca. 1930s), a response to Bergmann's work; H. Neurath (ca. 1940s), on protein chemistry; C. Niemann (2 files, ca. 1930s), various intellectual and institutional aspects of protein chemistry; J.H. Northrop** (2 files, 1930s–1940s), scientific correspondence; F. O'Flaherty (4 files, ca. 1930s–1940s) on leather research; W.J.V. Osterhout* (ca. 1940s), Bergmann's reaction to Osterhout's work; L. Pauling (ca. 1940), on Niemann's career; M. Perutz, letters referring to the Rockefeller Foundation; Protein Committee (ca. 1930s–1940s), on many scientific and organizational aspects of protein chemistry in America; Refugee Correspondence (1941); William J. Robbins*, on administrative issues; F.O. Schmitt (2 files, ca. 1930s–1940s), material on the state of protein chemistry; W. Stein (3 files, ca. 1930s–1940s), on various aspects of Stein's career; K.G. Stern, regarding Bergmann's joining the enzyme group; University of Michigan (ca. 1930s), on his summer lectures.

These files are supplemented by the Bergmann correspondence in the Flexner Papers* (1933–1942).

2. Cannon, Walter Bradford (1871–1945). Physiologist. APS 1908. Papers, ca. 1905–1928, 658 items.
(The major collection of W.B. Cannon Papers is at the Countway Library, Harvard.)

When Walter B. Cannon was chosen to succeed Henry P. Bowditch in 1906 as head of the Laboratory of Experimental Physiology at Harvard Medical School (the first laboratory of experimental physiology in America), he was already recognized as a leader in the field. A champion of scientific medicine and experimental biology, Cannon's neurophysiological studies on the regulation of the sympathetic nervous system, and his work on endocrine function, often entailed vivisection of animals (mainly cats). This of course was a motivating factor in his active participation in the effort against the anti-vivisection campaign.

Originating late in the nineteenth century, the legislative debates concerning vivisection, which continued well into the 1920s, transcended mere emotional issues of cruelty to animals. The opposition to experimental research in physiology threatened the image of the new establishment of scientific medicine, its public support and potential resources. This threat was a motivating force behind Cannon's opposition to the anti-vivisectionists.

The correspondence between William Williams Keen (APS president 1908–1918) and W.B. Cannon, which makes up most of this collection, deals almost exclusively with the anti-vivisection campaign and the legislative debate which it spawned. Although these papers do not address physiology research per se, they are a valuable source on aspects of the social and political context of experimental physiology and medicine.

This collection is complemented by the Cannon correspondence in the papers of Flexner* (8 files, 1910–1938), Rous*, and Clark*. These communications reflect Cannon's immense influence on the institutional aspects of the life sciences. File #8 in the Flexner Papers* is particularly informative about Cannon's views regarding the study of human behavior under the aegis of the Rockefeller Foundation's new biology program in the early 1930s and his advisory role within the Foundation.

3. Chargaff, Erwin (1905–   ). Biochemist. APS 1979.
Papers, ca. 1931–1971, ca. 30,000 items.

Erwin Chargaff was the first biochemist in America to develop a substantial research program centered around the genetic specificity of nucleic acids, research that formed a major chapter in the history of molecular biology. Having been one of a handful of life scientists in the mid-1940s to appreciate the significance of O.T. Avery's discovery that DNA was the transforming principle in pneumococci, Chargaff set out to probe the chemical properties of nucleic acids in relation to their biological specificity. By 1950 his finding that DNA could account for genetic specificity led to the demise of P.A.T. Levene's** dominant tetranucleotide theory of DNA structure, which regarded DNA as ill-suited for carrying information. Chargaff's findings also eclipsed some of Max Bergmann's* protein theories of biological specificity. Chargaff's work was a turning point in gene research from proteins to nucleic acids, and his laboratory at Columbia (in the biochemistry department headed by H.T. Clarke*) became a premier center for nucleic acids chemistry.

The Chargaff Papers document in detail the intellectual and social history of his research program. There are 46 boxes of personal and professional correspondence, and 23 boxes of manuscript drafts and calculations. The files, still in the order in which Chargaff had arranged them (roughly chronologically), are at present somewhat difficult to use. A detailed finding aid by P. Abir-Am has been prepared.

The collection contains records of Chargaff's investigations on rickettsia and typhus during the war years 1942–1945 as part of the OSRD projects, as well as material on his research on the chemistry of blood coagulants (Boxes 1–3); these are important sources on the relation of the life sciences to the military. There is a great deal of material on the crucial years 1945–1950, during which time Chargaff reoriented his research program toward the chemistry of heredity, and records that include rejections of his research proposals by several foundations (Boxes 3–4).

After 1950, with the increased interest in nucleic acids, Chargaff gained recognition and acquired his own research facilities at Columbia, the Laboratory of Cell Chemistry. Boxes 5–12 include material on nucleic acids research, the rise of molecular genetics, and Chargaff's role in these developments. Of interest are his exchanges with pharmaceutical houses (ca. 1940s–1950s), including Hoffmann-La Roche, Bio-Vin, Upjohn, Eli Lilly, Rohm and Haas, and Parke-Davis, communications highlighting the links between academic and industrial biochemistry. The remainder of the correspondence (1960s) reflects the expansion of Chargaff's administrative activities and his increased influence within the life sciences.

The major correspondents in this collection are: R.J. Anderson (Box 3, file 1; Box 5, file 1); W.T. Astbury (Box 12, file 1); J. Barzun (Box 28, file 7); E.D. Bergmann (Box 3, file 2; Box 5, file 2); K. Bernhard (Box 3, file 2); A. Bondi (Box 5, file 2); J. Brachet (Box 18, file 2); G. Brawerman (Box 13, file 2); S.S. Cohen (Box 5, file 3; Box 18, file 3); W.E. Cohn (Box 5, file 3; Box 10, file 4; Box 13, file 8; Box 18, file 3); Columbia University (Box 13, file 6); J.N. Davidson (Box 3, file 2; Box 6, file 1; Box 10, file 4; Box 29, file 12); P. Doty (Box 6, file 1); C. Ehrensvard (Box 13, file 9); D. Elson (Box 6, file 2; Box 10, file 6; Box 14, file 1; Box 18, file 5); A.C. Frazer (Box 3, file 3; Box 6, file 3; Box 10, file 7); G. Gamow (Box 6, file 4); T. Gustavson (Box 6, file 4); F. Haurowitz (Box 6, file 5; Box 10, file 10); J.N. Hawthorne (Box 6, file 5; Box 10, file 10; Box 19, file 5); S. Horstadius (Box 6, file 5); R.D. Hotchkiss (Box 6, file 5); J.C. Kendrew (Box 10, file 13; Box 11, file 13); J. Lederberg (Box 7, file 4; Box 16, file 3); K. Lindestrom-Lang (Box 7, file 4); A. Monroy (Box 7, file 5; Box 16, file 3); N.W. Pirie (Box 7, file 7; Box 11, file 4; Box 16, file 5; Box 19, file 10); M.R. Pollock (Box 16, file 5; Box 19, file 10); T. Reichenstein (Box 8, file 1); D. Rittenberg (Box 33, file 7); J. Runnstrom (Box 4, file 2; Box 17, file 6); J.J. Saukkonen (Box 11, file 7; Box 16, file 8; Box 20, file 1); G. Schmidt (Box 4, file 3; Box 8, file 2); E.C. Slater (Box 36, file 1); C. Tamm (Box 8, file 3; Box 20, file 2); A.R. Todd (Box 4, file 4; Box 8, file 3); R. Vendrely (Box 11, file 15; Box 20, file 4); E. Vischer (Box 11, file 15; Box 20, file 4); M.H.F. Wilkins (Box 11, file 17). There are a few interesting exchanges with F.H.C. Crick (early 1950s), and L. Pauling (late 1940s).

Unfortunately there is little material on Chargaff's years in Germany or the period 1934–1941, when he first established his research program at Columbia. But being a prolific writer and a vociferous critic of American culture, Chargaff frequently compared his European and American experiences. His correspondence with many European colleagues throughout the the 1940s and 1950s deals with issues surrounding the intellectual migration and reflects this cross-cultural perspective.

4. Clark, William Mansfield (1884–1964). Biochemist. APS 1939.
    Papers, ca. 1903–1964, ca. 7000 items, 24 notebooks (6 ln.ft.).

William Mansfield Clark headed the Department of Physiological Chemistry at the Johns Hopkins Medical School from 1927 to 1952, where he developed a major research program in physical biochemistry, centering around oxidation-reduction potentials of organic systems, research that required precise measurements and sensitive instruments. The Clark Papers contain material relating to his lectures and papers, twenty-four notebooks (1941–1953), ten files on his associate Barnett Cohen (1910s–1950s) that include extensive data on dyes, and two photograph files containing pictures of his laboratory, the "Temple of pH." There are also four student notebooks (physical chemistry, optics, thermodynamics/physics), which together with the correspondence, form a rich record on laboratory practice and training in physical biochemistry.

Clark's correspondence files include communications with American chemists, biochemists, and physiologists, among them Roger Adams (ca. 1940s), on activities related to World War II; Rudolph J. Anderson (ca. 1930s), on matters related to Clark's editorship of the *Journal of Biological*

Chemistry; Eric Ball** (ca. 1930s–1960s); R.K. Cannan (ca. 1920s–1930s), reflections on Clark's program and his place within biochemistry; W.B. Cannon* (1930s), administrative communications; James B. Conant (1920s–1940s), technical correspondence; Roger M. Herriott (1940s); Jacques Loeb** (1920), professional exchanges; Leonor Michaelis (1920s–1950s), professional exchanges; Albert W. Noyes (1920s–1960s); A.N. Richards (1920s–1950s), administrative correspondence; Donald D. Van Slyke** (3 files, 1920s–1950s), scientific and administrative correspondence; Hubert B. Vickery (2 files, 1940s–1960s), scientific and administrative communications; Vincent Du Vigneaud** (1950s); and H. Wieland** (1920s); as well as exchanges with the European biochemists Joseph Needham (1920s), S.P.L. Sorensen (1920s), and Hugo Theorell (1950s). The files on Eric Ball**, Edward A. Park (1930s), and Otto Warburg (1940s) reveal episodes and attitudes (including anti-Semitism) related to the intellectual migration.

Before coming to Johns Hopkins, Clark had worked in bacterial chemistry at the United States Department of Agriculture and in the United States Public Health Service, where he was made chief of the Division of Chemistry of the Hygienic Laboratory. A few files (records dated before 1927) contain information on the practice of biochemistry and microbiology within federal bureaus.

Clark's career, as seen from his papers, exemplifies the disciplinary evolution from medical chemistry to biochemistry. As the founders of American biochemistry sought to liberate their field from a clinical service-role, they increasingly allied it with the physical sciences; Clark's skills in physical biochemistry—his hydrogen ion determinations, and his studies of buffers and salts in connection with bacterial fermentation—were well suited to the new orientation. This reorientation is documented in correspondence files on J.J. Abel, W. Pepper, and A.N. Richards (1920s), and in a 1927 letter about Clark's appointment in the "Unknown" #2 file.

During his tenure at Johns Hopkins, Clark assumed leadership of his profession. He was on the editorial board of the *Journal of Biological Chemistry* and served as president of both the Society of American Bacteriologists and the American Society of Biological Chemists. The materials on Johns Hopkins University (4 files, 1909–1955), on the Society of American Bacteriologists (6 files, 1927–1955), and on the American Society of Biological Chemists (1931–57) document important institutional aspects of the rise of American biochemistry. Clark's correspondence with Isaiah Bowman (1930s–1940s), Detlev W. Bronk (1940s–1950s), Vannevar Bush (1940s), J.B. Conant (1920s–1940s), and A.N. Richards (1920s–1950s) shows him to have been an active member of the scientific establishment that emerged during World War I and shaped American science well into the 1950s.

5. Clarke, Hans Thacher (1887–1972). Biochemist. APS 1943.
   Papers, ca. 1903–1973, ca. 3500 items (3 ln.ft.).

The appointment of Hans Thacher Clarke as chairman of the biochemistry department of Columbia's College of Physicians and Surgeons in 1928 signaled a disciplinary shift away from a clinical orientation toward a biochemistry firmly rooted in organic and physical chemistry. In urging him to assume the chairmanship, James Conant wrote to Clarke, "Here is a Medical Group that at last have seen the light and want a straight organic chemist to run the show" (Box 3, 23 May 1928).

Clarke's background in academic and industrial organic chemistry had had little connection to medical problems. A protégé of William Ramsay at University College in London, and later a student of Emil Fischer, Clarke specialized in the synthesis of proteins. During World War I and until his move to Columbia, Clarke engaged in research and development of photographic chemicals at Eastman Kodak, retaining a consultantship with Kodak until 1969 (3 files, ca. 60 items, 1912–1963). During these years Clarke acquired a reputation among organic chemists as a superb organizer of research.

His administrative skills and ability to recognize talent contributed to the growth of Columbia's biochemistry department, which by the 1940s had become one of the largest and most influential in the United States. The correspondence with Clarke's mentor A.W. Stewart (ca. 20 items, 1926–1935) contains materials regarding the development of the new department. The file "Biochemistry at Columbia" (1955) includes a list of doctorates granted from 1913 to 1957, with the positions of the graduates in 1955. In addition to correspondence, the collection contains laboratory notebooks from 1928 to 1971.

During the 1930s, Clarke opened his laboratory to refugee biochemists, among them E. Brand, E. Chargaff* (ca. 1940s–1950s); Z. Dische, K. Meyer, D. Nachmansohn (ca. 10 items, 1961–1969), R. Schoenheimer, and H. Waelsch. Unfortunately, the correspondence does not reflect the scope of these activities. The Chargaff* file contains material reflecting Clarke's influence and popularity among his students and colleagues.

Other correspondents include: Roger Adams (3 items, 1947–1968); Detlev W. Bronk; Vincent Du Vigneaud**; Joseph S. Fruton (7 items, 1955–1972); William J. Gies (letters related to biographical material on Gies); Sir Julian Huxley (17 letters, 1958–1972); J. Murray Luck (9 letters, 1956–1965); Samuel Smiles (15 items, 1926–1934); William Shockley (2 files, 1968–1970); Sir Geoffrey Taylor (ca. 30 items, 1955–1972); and Merle Tuve (biographical material on Clarke).

In addition to Clarke's central role in developing biochemistry at

Columbia, the collection documents the broad range of his professional activities in the National Academy of Sciences (3 files, 1942–1963); the American Chemical Society (3 files, 1956–1966); the American Society of Biological Chemists (5 files, 1942–1963); and the the Merck Fellowship Board (1957, regarding his chairmanship).

6.   Cohn, Mildred (1913–   ). Biochemist, biophysicist. APS 1972.
     Papers, 1947–1980, ca. 12,000 items (19 ln.ft.).

The career of Mildred Cohn developed during a time when the Rockefeller Foundation was funneling millions of dollars into physico-chemical biology, with a primary interest in the laboratories where Cohn conducted her researches. Mildred Cohn received her doctorate in physical chemistry from Columbia University in 1938, completing her graduate work under Harold C. Urey on the biological uses of stable isotopes. She continued her research at Cornell under V. Du Vigneaud**, where she established an isotope laboratory for investigations of various metabolic processes. From 1946 to 1960 Cohn worked in the laboratory of Carl and Gerty Cori (Nobel laureates in 1947 for studies of glycogen metabolism) at Washington University, continuing her studies of enzymatic mechanisms with the use of isotopes. In 1953 she began working with the new technique of nuclear magnetic resonance (NMR), which remained her active research area at the Johnson Foundation and Department of Biophysics at the University of Pennsylvania.

     The Cohn collection includes correspondence, research data (20 notebooks), reviews of grant proposals (NSF, Research Corporation), manuscripts, and student recommendations (restricted); however, there is almost no record of her career prior to the early 1950s. The correspondence includes scientific communications with: Paul D. Boyer; Britton Chance** (3 files, ca. 1960s); Carl and Gerty Cori; V. Du Vigneaud** (ca. 1960s–1970s); Du Pont de Nemours and Co. (ca. 1960s); Manfred Eigen (ca. 1960s); Arthur Kornberg (ca. 1950s); Daniel Koshland (ca. 1960s); Hans Krebs (ca. late 1950s and early 1960s); Stanley L. Miller (Urey file, 1960s–1970s); and Albert Szent-Gyorgyi (1961). These materials are a rich source on the role of instruments and laboratory techniques in biochemistry and biophysics.

     The papers of Mildred Cohn are especially informative on the early uses of NMR applications to biological systems, and on the development of that important technology from the early 1950s to the mid-1970s. There are files on Gordon Conferences on NMR (1964–1971), on the International Conferences on NMR (7 files, 1960s–1970s), numerous files under NMR, and correspondence with Varian Instruments (1960–1975), the first commercial manufacturer of NMR instruments. These files, complemented by correspondence with Cohn's colleagues, form a substantial record of the history of NMR technology in the life sciences and the history of biophysics.

7. Cold Spring Harbor, New York. Biological Laboratory.
Records, 1958–1965, ca. 100 pp.

The history of the Cold Spring Harbor laboratories began in 1904 with the Station for Experimental Evolution (later renamed Department of Genetics), sponsored by the Carnegie Institution of Washington. In 1924, the Long Island Biological Association established a summer research institute on the Station's grounds that soon emphasized physico-chemical biology. The Cold Spring Harbor summer symposia in quantitative biology, which began in 1933, became intellectual markers in physiology, biochemistry, and biophysics. In the early 1940s, under the energetic directorship of Milislav Demerec*, the Department of Genetics and the Cold Spring Harbor Laboratories were consolidated, becoming by the late 1940s an international center of molecular genetics. Due in part to the catalytic growth of the symposia and research activities, the 1950s were a time of reorganization, to equip the Cold Spring Harbor Laboratories better for its leadership role in the life sciences.

Apart from brief historical accounts, the Cold Spring Harbor Collection provides little material on the formative years of the laboratory, but it does document the second phase of its history. The material in the Cold Spring Harbor Collection includes correspondence (M. Demerec*, W.H. Page, and E.L. Tatum), reports, and minutes of meetings. The collection is complemented by the Demerec Papers*, which contain sources on the earlier history of Cold Spring Harbor, and by the Charles Davenport Papers at the APS Library, which contain two series of Cold Spring Harbor records from its earlier phase.

8. Demerec, Milislav (1895–1966). Geneticist. APS 1952.
Papers, 1919–1966, ca. 10,000 items (18 ln.ft.).

Milislav Demerec came to the United States from Yugoslavia in 1919 and joined the Department of Plant Breeding at Cornell, where he studied variegation of maize. In 1923 Demerec began his career at Cold Spring Harbor* as a staff member of the Department of Genetics of the Carnegie Institution of Washington, later expanding his research interests to include studies of Delphiniums, *Drosophila*, and radiation genetics.

In the early 1940s Demerec became director of the Long Island Biological Association Laboratory and the Department of Genetics. Under his leadership the two scientific groups were in effect combined, and Cold

Spring Harbor became an institution where genetics intersected with research in physico-chemical biology. It was a center especially noted for its summer phage courses and symposia in quantitative biology. By the time of Demerec's retirement in 1960, Cold Spring Harbor had become an international center of molecular biology.

Unfortunately there are no files on the summer symposia, but there is some related material. In order to organize summer research and conferences, Demerec communicated with researchers from several areas in the life sciences. Therefore, in addition to files on his activities in classical genetics—professional organizations, lectures, correspondence with geneticists, and over sixty laboratory notebooks—the Demerec Collection contains records of his involvement with the new physico-chemical biology, and material on conferences and international congresses.

The correspondents include: Harold A. Abramson (2 files, 1957–1960); E.B. Babcock; George W. Beadle (1920s–1950s); Albert F. Blakeslee; Calvin B. Bridges (7 files, 1931–1949); Detlev W. Bronk; Ernst W. Caspari; William E. Castle; Edward U. Condon; Charles B. Davenport; Max Delbrück; Theodosius Dobzhansky (7 files, 1929–1957); Rollins Emerson (ca. 80 items, 1923–1947); Boris Ephrussi (1930s–1950s); Richard B. Goldschmidt; J.B.S. Haldane (1930s–1950s); Alexander Hollaender*; Charles W. Metz; Henry A. Moe; Hermann J. Muller; Tracy Sonneborn; Lewis Stadler; A.H. Sturtevant; N.W. Timoféeff-Ressovsky (2 files, mostly from the 1930s); M.A. Tuve (ca. 30 items, 1936–1947); and Harold Urey.

9. Flexner, Simon (1863–1946). Bacteriologist, pathologist, administrator. APS 1901.
Papers, ca. 1891–1946, ca. 175,000 items (163 ln.ft.).

Simon Flexner was one of the most influential figures in the life sciences in America, and a prominent member of the scientific establishment that shaped the country's intellectual and social development. Major aspects of this growth are documented in this voluminous collection, which includes correspondence, diaries (ca. 1900, 1915–1944), laboratory notebooks (ca. 1900–1920), and drafts of articles and addresses.

The early phases of Flexner's academic career—his medical education at the University of Louisville, his subsequent move to Johns Hopkins (1890–1899), and his tenure at the University of Pennsylvania as professor of pathology (1899–1906)—are not covered in this collection (however, a number of secondary sources fill these gaps). *A Guide to Selected Files of The Professional Papers of Simon Flexner at the American Philosophical Society Library* by Margaret Miller (APS, 1979) describes parts of the collection in detail. The entry on Flexner in this bibliography therefore addresses only those files which bear on the intellectual and institutional development of physiology, biochemistry, and biophysics. Files that are substantial enough to form manuscript sources on researchers in these disciplines are annotated separately in the secondary group.

Flexner influenced the growth of physiology, biochemistry, and biophysics in two ways: as director of the Rockefeller Institute, and through his positions of leadership in the Rockefeller Foundation, the National Research Council, the Carnegie Foundation and other scientific organizations and journals; his professional papers reflect both aspects of his influence. The major correspondents within these scientific spheres are: E. Abderhalden (5 files, 1911–1934), on physiological and biochemical research in Germany and at the Kaiser-Wilhelm Institute; Roger Adams (10 items, 1929–1934); Jerome Alexander (20 items, 1916–1934), on colloid chemistry; C.L. Alsberg (15 items, 1913–1920), material on USDA Bureau of Chemistry; O.T. Avery (3 files, 1913–1945), administrative communications; F.G. Banting (ca. 50 items, 1923–1937), on the production of insulin; Max Bergmann* (35 items, 1933–1942), scientific and administrative correspondence; Niels Bohr (4 items, 1938), on the relation of physics to biology; W.B. Cannon*; E.J. Cohn**; Carnegie Institution (5 files, 1911–1915); P. Lecomte Du Noüy (60 items, 1919–1937), correspondence on x-ray crystallography, and on molecular physics at the Pasteur Institute; D. Edsall (3 files, 1910–1930); W.R. Embree (24 files, 1917–1936), on the Rockefeller Foundation's support of the life sciences; W.O. Fenn (20 items, 1921–1924), plans for work in biophysics and physiology; M. Heidelberger (2 files, 1913–1943); Johns Hopkins University School of Hygiene and Public Health (3 files, 1916–1925); K. Landsteiner* (3 files, 1914–1937), administrative communications; P.A.T. Levene**; F.R. Lillie*; J. Loeb**; A.S. Loevenhart (45 items, 1910–1929), physiology and pharmacology at the University of Wisconsin; O. Meyerhoff (25 items, 1923–1934); L. Michaelis (50 items, 1920–1937, 1945); A.E. Mirsky (12 items, 1927–1934, 1944), scientific and administrative correspondence; T.H. Morgan (2 files, 1919–1935), general correspondence; J.B. Murphy (10 files, 1915–1939), communications on cancer research and administrative concerns; National Research Council (24 files, 1916–1945); J.H. Northrop**; P.K. Olitsky* (7 files, 1917–1939), work on viruses; W.J.V. Osterhout* (40 items, 1927–1941), scientific and administrative material; T.M. Rivers* (4 files, 1922–1949), virus diseases; Rockefeller Foundation (9 files, 1913–1934); Rockefeller Institute (20 files, 1914-1939); Rockefeller Sanitary Commission (1 file, 1910); Wickliffe Rose (24 files, 1910–1931), correspondence on the International Health Board and support of the natural sciences by the Rockefeller Foundation; F.P. Rous* (11 files, 1916–1941), administrative correspondence mainly about the *Journal of Experimental Medicine*; F.R. Sabin (4 files, 1913–1940), general correspondence; W.M. Stanley** (18 items, 1935–

1941); O. Warburg (25 items, 1924–1931); W.H. Welch (14 files, 1910–1932), scientific and administrative correspondence; E. Beecher Wilson* (3 files, 1915–1939), relation between research in the life sciences and support by insurance companies; D.D. Van Slyke**; R.W.G. Wyckoff**; and H. Zinsser (11 files, 1913–1935), administrative correspondence and scientific communications on virus research and immunology.

10. Hollaender, Alexander (1898–1985). Biophysicist, geneticist.
     Papers, ca. 1950–1970, ca. 4000 items (8 ln.ft.).

Alexander Hollaender was educated at the University of Wisconsin, receiving his doctorate in physical chemistry in 1931. These were exciting times to be at Wisconsin, surrounded by scientists like Max Mason, Warren Weaver, J.W. Williams**, and T. Svedberg**, men who in the early 1930s would spearhead the merger of physics, chemistry, and biology under the aegis of the Rockefeller Foundation. Hollaender became an active participant in these intellectual and institutional endeavors. He remained associated with Wisconsin until 1937, working on problems of radiation genetics and chemical mutagenesis (he was one of the first researchers to point out the significance of nucleic acids in mutagenesis). He was also an adviser to the Rockefeller Foundation on the development of molecular biology, and was involved in administering Rockefeller Fellowships and projects of the National Research Council.

In 1937 Hollaender moved to the Washington Biophysics Institute of the National Institutes of Health as an associate biologist, and soon after was promoted as senior biophysicist, a position he held until 1950. By that time Hollaender had established himself as a world authority on radiation genetics. He served as director of the division of biology at the Atomic Energy Commission's Oak Ridge National Laboratory from 1946 to 1966, and as a senior research adviser from 1967 until his retirement in 1972. His personal papers have been deposited at the University of Tennessee.

The Hollaender Papers at the APS Library document his activities in postwar radiation genetics, a field addressing biological problems in relation to the newly unleashed powers of atomic energy. There are 30 files containing records of the National Academy's Committee on the Biological Effects of Atomic Radiation, and 41 files on the Second International Conference on the Peaceful Uses of Atomic Energy. As an active member of the World Health Organization (WHO), Hollaender headed a Study Group on the Effects of Radiation on Human Genetics, activities recorded in approximately 30 files. There is also material on the 1958 Symposium on Genetics in Medical Research, and material on more current issues (1960s) in genetics and molecular biology, such as the International Conference on Replication and Recombination of Genetic Material (7 files, ca. 1960s), and records on the Workshop on Space Radiation Biology (1965).

The main correspondents in this collection are : G.W. Beadle, D.W. Bronk, C.I. Campbell, M. Demerec*, T. Dobzhansky, S. Emerson, J. Lederberg, H.J. Muller, J.V. Neel, Max Perutz, C. Stern, A.H. Sturtevant, and W. Weaver. These communications, together with the files on radiation genetics, form an important source on the history of that field and its relations to social concerns, environmental issues, and cancer research.

11. Landsteiner, Karl (1868–1943). Medical researcher, immunologist. APS 1935.
Biographical data, ca. 650 items.

When Landsteiner left Vienna in 1922 at the age of fify-four to join the Rockefeller Institute, he had already done much of his most important work. In the early years of the century he had discovered a simple technique of agglutination, whereby human blood was divided into four groups, a discovery that made possible safe blood transfusions. This work, in turn, led him to the study of hereditary differences in antigens of blood groups, and thus to the birth of serological genetics. A succession of discoveries followed in the 1920s and 1930s, after he had moved to the Rockefeller Institute: the discovery of blood factors (M,N,P, and Rh factors), and investigations on the chemical specificity of serological reactions, which became a basis of immunochemistry. Landsteiner was awarded the Nobel Prize in Physiology or Medicine in 1930.

After Landsteiner's death, George M. Mackenzie began collecting materials for a biography: correspondence with friends and associates of Landsteiner, memoranda of conversations, notes and recollections of Landsteiner by T.M. Rivers* (1944–1952) and by Max Neuberger, annual reports from Landsteiner's laboratory at the Institute (1923–43), correspondence on publications and the Nobel Prize, and raw material on immunology and the study of blood. These materials comprise the Landsteiner Collection (the biography was never completed). Of special interest are records on medical education in Vienna, the growth of anti-Semitism, and correspondence with Simon Flexner* which led to Landsteiner's move to the Institute.

The collection is eclectic and contains large gaps (many scribbled notes), but it is useful as a supplemental background source on Landsteiner. The collection is complemented by the Landsteiner correspondence in the Flexner Papers* (3 files, 1914–1937), which contains administrative and scientific material on Landsteiner's laboratory. There is also substantial material on Landsteiner in the Rous Papers* (5 files, 1920s–1940s).

12. Lewis, Warren Harmon (1870–1964). Cytologist. APS 1943.
Papers, ca. 1913–1964, ca. 8000 items (8 ln.ft.).

Between the 1910s and 1930s, Warren Harmon Lewis (together with his wife and colleague Margaret Lewis) developed methods of tissue culture and means of observation which revolutionized the field of cytology. While still at the Anatomical Laboratory at Johns Hopkins (1903–1919), the Lewises prepared a simple fluid which enabled them to grow cells in culture dishes and thus observe previously hidden details of cell structure and physiological activities. They continued their cytological studies at the Embryology Department of the Carnegie Institution (located in Baltimore) until their move to the Wistar Institute in Philadelphia after 1940.

Warren Lewis's research program focused mainly on morphological aspects of cell structure, cell division, cell locomotion, and phagocytosis, in normal as well as in cancer cells. In 1929 he was first to develop time-lapse microscopic motion pictures to record observations on living cells in culture. His films became important teaching resources in cytology, and led him to develop mechanical theories of cell motion. Lewis was president of the American Association of Anatomists (1934–1936) and of the International Society for Experimental Cytology (1939–1947).

The Lewis Papers are primarily from the 1930s to the 1950s and consist of two divisions: correspondence and laboratory records. The correspondence documents his cytological studies and motion picture research on cells, as well as his activities in professional societies. The experimental materials include lectures, experiments, drawings, photographs, and film scripts, covering a wide range of topics in embryology, cytology, oncology, and immunology.

The correspondence section contains several files on the American Association of Anatomists, which include communications with leading scientists surrounding the 1935 symposium on "The Relation of the Anterior Pituitary to Reproduction", among them G.W. Corner, F.L. Hisaw, A.E. Severinghaus*, and E.T. Engle. There is material on the International Society for Experimental Cytology (3 files, 1938–1947), which includes correspondence with J. Runnstrom, R.G. Harrison, R. Chambers, and D.W. Bronk; a file on the American Institute of Biological Sciences (1950), and on the Institut International d'Embryologie (1930s–1950s). Other important correspondents are: W.C. Alvarez (1937–1939), on various research problems in cytology; D.W. Bronk (1940), on reviewing a paper in biophysics; V. Bush (1930s–1950s), material on the Carnegie Institution and the Berkeley cyclotron; T. Caspersson** (1939), communications regarding a Rockefeller Fellowship for the study of DNA; C.B. Davenport (1930s); M. Demerec*; W.B. Hardy (1930), on colloid science; A. Hollaender* (1939); E.E. Just (1930s), on embryological research; C. Metz (1941), on embryology; F.R.

Sabin; F. Schrader (1940s), on cytogenetics and cellular fusion; M. Schram (1940s), on international cancer research; and the Wistar Institute (1940s–1960s), numerous files on research and administrative issues at the Institute.

13.　Neuberg, Carl (1877–1956). Biochemist.
　　Papers, ca. 1929–1956, ca. 10,000 items (12 ln.ft.).

Carl Neuberg was one of Germany's most important biochemists, from intellectual, institutional, and commercial standpoints. His investigations were reflected in over 900 publications covering sugar chemistry, fermentation processes, enzyme chemistry, amino acid studies, and phenomena of biochemical reduction and phosphorylation in living cells. He was the founder and editor of the *Biochemische Zeitschrift* (1906), and from the early 1920s until 1937 was director of the Kaiser-Wilhelm Institute for Experimental Therapy and of the Kaiser-Wilhelm Institute for Biochemistry.

After being ousted by the Hitler regime, Neuberg's odyssey through Holland, Palestine, Iraq, Iran, India, and New Guinea finally brought him to New York in 1940 at the age of sixty-three. With the exception of correspondence with his friend Kurt Jacobson in Portugal (5 files, 1929–1956), with a few German industries (4 files, ca. 1916–1945), with the Kaiser Wilhelm Society and Institutes (5 files, ca. 1913- 1952), and with the German War Department (2 files, 1916) the Neuberg Papers (correspondence, laboratory notebooks, documents, photographs, and reprints) date from his arrival in America.

According to Neuberg, he had arrived "ten years too late to find a proper position". Relative to other prominent émigré biochemists (Bergmann*, Chargaff*, Schoenheimer, etc.), Neuberg did not fare well in his new country. The tiny laboratory at New York University and the facilities he later obtained at Brooklyn Polytechnic Institute were inadequate for a substantial research program. He continued to investigate problems of relevance to commercial chemical processes, especially in the pharmaceutical and fermentation industries. There are about 35 correspondence files documenting his contacts with commercial houses, among them Anheuser-Busch (1942–1956); Carbide and Carbon Chemicals Co. (1942–1953); Federal Yeast Corporation (1943–1956); Hoffmann-La Roche (1944–1954); Lederle Laboratories (1943–1949); Monsanto Chemical Co. (1942–1948); National Grain Yeast Corp. (1942–1949); National Sugar Refining Co. (1944–1952); Rohm and Haas Co. (1942–1948); E.R. Squibb and Sons (1948–1953); and Standard Oil Co. (1946–1948).

Neuberg also continued his fundamental research in cell chemistry, with moderate support from private and public sources. His studies on solubility and transport phenomena in cells and tissues were relevant to several fields in the life sciences, such as agriculture, nutrition, cytology, and oncology, leading to projects supported by the United States government. The files on government-sponsored research contain a wealth of information—proposals, contracts, progress reports, and letters—highlighting the growing linkages between the life sciences, government, and the military during the postwar era.

Of special interest is the correspondence with the American Cancer Society (5 files, 1949–1956); the Nutrition Foundation (1943–1945); the Rockefeller Foundation (1941), grant application and rejection; U.S. Atomic Energy Commission (3 files, 1949–1953), grant applications and approval of projects on solubility and metabolism of soil metals; U.S. Department of Agriculture (2 files, 1944–1950); Office of Naval Research (4 files, 1950–1955), proposals, reports, renewals, and contracts on cell transport projects; U.S. Public Health Service (8 files, 1943–1955), on grants for phosphorous compounds and solubility in cells.

Throughout his life in the United States, Neuberg remained attached to European science and to international causes in science. Aside from founding the American Society of European Chemists (1 file, 1948-1954), he maintained correspondence with scientists from other countries, including Japan. Neuberg's correspondence with prominent German chemists (in German) is very informative on postwar German science, issues surrounding the intellectual migration, and Neuberg's misfortune in particular.

The main correspondents are: E. Abderhalden (1945–1949), on differences between American and German science, and on Max Bergmann*; R. Adams (1946–1948), on Adams's impressions of postwar Germany; L. Anschütz (1948–1955); H.C.S. Aron (2 files, 1942–1955); A. Butenandt** (1947–1956); H.J. Deuticke (1951–1956); H. von Euler (1947–1956); H. Fromageot (1940–1953); H. Gaffron (1943–1956), on research interests, and technical and social issues; Otto Hahn (1947–1956), on issues related to Neuberg's directorship of the Kaiser-Wilhelm Institute; K. Jacobson (5 files, 1924–1956), scientific, professional, and personal communications; D. Mazia (1955–1956), on Neuberg's difficult times in America; Otto Meyerhoff (1947–1949); L. Michaelis (1947-1949); D. Nachmanson (1947–1945); F.F. Nord (1942-1956); Severo Ochoa (1947–1955), on important aspects of Ochoa's career; K.G. Stern (1943 -1956), on interesting professional issues; Otto Warburg (1948–1956); H. Wieland** (1946–1955), on German and American chemistry and common colleagues.

14. Olitsky, Peter Kosciusko (1866–1964). Pathologist, microbiologist.
     Papers, 1917–1964, ca. 2500 items.

The career of Peter K. Olitsky at the Rockefeller Institute for Medical Research spanned more than three decades, a period that included basic research in virology, biomedical war projects (World Wars I and II), travel to Europe and to China to investigate viral epidemics, and work on animal and plant viruses for the United States Department of Agriculture. The collection documents these major aspects of Olitsky's career.

The papers are a good source for tracing important episodes in virology research, such as studies of plant and animal viruses, neurotropic viruses, the problem of poliomyelitis, and aspects related to the development of the Sabin and Salk vaccines. The material on virus research includes correspondence with J. Bronfenbrenner; P. Rous* (3 files, 1920–1940s); A. Sabin (13 files, 1930s–1940s); R.H. Yager (4 files, 1930s); R. Wyckoff**; H. Zinsser (1920–1930s); and a file on foot-and-mouth disease (1920s). There are also communications with A.C. Abbott (1920); E. Abderhalden (1920s); H.L. Amoss; W.B. Cannon* (1930s); A. Carrel; P. De Kruif; H.S. Gasser; F.L. Gates; F. Horsfall; I.M. Morgan (6 files); and T. M. Rivers*. In addition to correspondence, there is material on Olitsky's laboratory research, including records of experiments and development of vaccines, and medical war research.

The collection is also a valuable source on the relation of microbiology to government projects and military needs. Of special interest is the correspondence with Olitsky's colleague from the United States Public Health Service, H.R. Cox (7 files, 1920s), and with L. Boez (3 files), documenting the work on foot-and-mouth disease; the U.S. War Department (2 files on work during World War I); and World War II Commission Report (9 files).

The Olitsky collection contains 11 files of correspondence with Simon Flexner*, and is complemented by the Flexner Papers*, which contain 7 files (1917–1939) on Olitsky, relating to viral epidemics Olitsky was investigating, research on plant and animal viruses, and Olitsky's scientific travels.

15. Osterhout, John Van Leuven (1871–1964). Physiologist. APS 1917. Papers, 1894–1961, ca. 2500 items (3 ln.ft.).

The Osterhout Collection records the scientific career of Winthrop John Van Leuven Osterhout from the turn of the century to the 1950s. The correspondence, drafts of papers, lectures, and photographs document significant trends in American life sciences. Having begun at the botany department at Brown University, Osterhout continued working in botany at Berkeley (where he completed his doctorate in 1899) on problems of cell division in plants. While a professor of botany at Harvard (1909–1924) he began his innovative research program on the physico-chemical properties of membranes and cytoplasm of algae cells. He expanded this program (related to neurophysiology) after succeeding his late mentor Jacques Loeb** in 1924 as head of the physiology department at the Rockefeller Institute. During these years Osterhout was also associated with the marine laboratories in Pacific

Grove, Woods Hole, and Bermuda, and with the Agassiz Museum; he was also a founding editor of the *Journal of General Physiology*.

As his papers show, Osterhout's scientific path bridged two major intellectual traditions: the agricultural and the medical, linking studies in botany and zoology with the new discipline of general physiology. His research program also reflected the shift in emphasis from morphological to physico-chemical problems in physiology. Indeed, his studies at the Rockefeller Institute of membrane permeability and bio-electric phenomena merged important areas in biochemistry, biophysics, and physiology (especially neurophysiology), as is reflected in his correspondence with other leaders in these fields.

The correspondents include: J.J. Abel (1925); E. Abderhalden (1936); American Association for the Advancement of Science (1913), on the organization of sessions in plant physiology; American Society of Plant Physiology (1926–1927), with material on European research; Svante Arrhenius** (1906–1924), many long letters from Arrhenius on topics in physical chemistry and biophysics, cultural issues, institutional involvements, Nobel Prizes, politics, the war and the international scientific community; M. Bergmann* (1942); Bioelectric Potentials (1946), conference papers; B. Brierly (1925), including a significant document on the organization of the Rothamsted Experimental Station, and correspondence on postwar conditions in England; L. Burbank (1897–1909), on plant breeding; W.B. Cannon* (1920s and 1930s), scientific correspondence; K.S. Cole (1946–1959), on biophysics; J.B. Conant (interwar period), scientific correspondence; W.J. Crozier (ca. 1920s–1950s), on the organization of research in the life sciences; H. De Vries (1902–1935), impressions of American research institutions of life sciences; F.G. Donnan (1929–1937), on plant physiology; S. Flexner* (1924–1940, ca. 200 items), on major trends in cytology, physiology, neurophysiology, and biophysics, and progress reports; J. Kirkwood (1942–1955), scientific exchanges; F.R. Lillie** (1920s–1930s), informative letters on Woods Hole; J. Loeb** (1909–1922), a great deal about scientific, administrative, and personal aspects of Loeb's tenure at Berkeley; J.C. Merriam (1925–1926), on research at the Tortuga Station; T.H. Morgan (1924–1926), administrative correspondence; J.H. Northrop** (1934–1964), scientific correspondence and editorial communications; E. O'Neill (1910), an important letter about Loeb and developing the life sciences at Berkeley; W.J.V. Osterhout (ca. 10 files, 1899–1961), including records on the Bermuda Station, administrative issues in general physiology, and Osterhout's Ph.D. thesis on pre-Mendelian chromosome research; G.H. Parker (1913–1956), general physiology at Harvard, and science and politics; H. Shapley (1928–1954), general physiology and politics at Harvard. This correspondence is complemented by the Osterhout file (1927–1941) of scientific and administrative correspondence in the Flexner Papers*.

16. Rivers, Thomas Milton (1888–1962). Medical virologist. APS 1942. Papers, ca. 1941–1963, ca. 10,000 items (11 ln.ft.).

Thomas Milton Rivers came to the hospital of the Rockefeller Institute in 1922 with the aim of establishing a research program in the new field of viral diseases. During the following fifteen years Rivers conducted studies on chicken pox and on viruses which cause psittacosis, poliomyelitis, and lymphocytic choriomeningitis, and developed methods for producing a smallpox vaccine for use in children. When Rivers was made director of the Institute's hospital in 1937, he was a world authority on virus research, a field that was then undergoing rapid growth as part of the nascent molecular biology program. During his directorship (1937–1955), Rivers was an active coordinator of medical war projects, and a principal organizer of research programs within the National Foundation for Infantile Paralysis (N.F.I.P); the N.F.I.P. became a major pursuit after his retiring from the Institute. Due to Rivers's prominence and his wide range of administrative activities, his papers include correspondence with many leading researchers and administrators in the life sciences, especially with those in fields related to microbiology and molecular biology. However, the correspondence with individuals tends to be brief and formal, touching mainly on administrative concerns. Furthermore, because the collection begins in 1940, there is little of substance (apart from early laboratory notes) to document the earlier stage of Rivers's scientific career. However, the Flexner Papers* include 4 files (1922–1949), which contain records on Rivers's virus research, and on administrative aspects of his department and the hospital.

The correspondents include: C.H. Andrewes, O.T. Avery, F.C. Bawden, D.W. Bronk, M. Burnet, J.M. Cattell, S. Cohen, E.J. Cohn**, M. Delbrück, M. Demerec*, R. Dubos, R. Dulbecco, V. Du Vigneaud**, A. Gratia, A. Gregg, A.D. Hershey, A. Hollaender*, F. Horsfall, S.E. Luria, A. Lwoff, W.J.V. Osterhout*, A. Sabin (4 files 1950s), J. Salk (9 files, 1950s–1960s), W.M. Stanley**, E.L. Tatum, A. Tiselius**, and H. Zinsser.

In spite of their limitations, the Rivers Papers are a valuable source in four areas: 1) the growth of American institutions of the life sciences in the postwar era, 2) biomedical war research and the Navy, 3) the development of virology, and 4) research on poliomyelitis and the development of the Salk vaccine.

Selected files documenting the first area are: American Public Health Association, Guggenheim Foundation, National Academy of Sciences (6 files), National Institutes of Health (4 files), National Research Council (3 files), Public Health Research Institute (15 files), Rockefeller Institute (ca. 25 files).

Selected files in the second area are: Armed Forces Epidemiological Board (3 files), History of U.S. Medical Research Unit No. 2 (5 files), U.S. Department of Defense (3 files), U.S. Department of Navy (8 files).

Selected files in the third area are: Conference on Inactivation of Viruses, Conference on Tissue Culture, Conference on Virus-Host Cell Relationships, International Congresses for Microbiology (4 files), T.M. Rivers (ca. 20 files on general aspects of virus research).

Selected files in the fourth area are: International Poliomyelitis Congresses (4 files), N.F.I.P. (ca. 20 files), B. O'Connor (7 files), Poliomyelitis (6 files), A. Sabin (4 files), J. Salk (9 files).

17. Robbins, William Jacob (1890–1978). Botanist, plant physiologist.
APS 1941.
Papers, 1898–1974, ca. 1500 items.

William Jacob Robbins was a highly influential member of the scientific establishment that came into being after World War I. His research focused on culture methods of plants in relation to biochemistry and nutrition, especially on the synthetic abilities of fungi. His studies, which emphasized a physico-chemical approach to botany, paralleled the scientific agenda of the Rockefeller Foundation, an agency with which he was closely associated for years as adviser and trustee.

His most important influence was in the organization and administration of scientific research. Beginning as professor of botany and chairman of the botany department at the University of Missouri in 1919, Robbins went on to become dean and president. While on leave from the University of Missouri, he was a member of the European Office of the Rockefeller Foundation (1928–1930), and was chairman of the National Research Council (NRC) Fellowship Board in the Biological Sciences (1931–1937). From 1937 until 1957 Robbins was director of the New York Botanical Garden and professor of botany at Columbia University; he was also president of the American Philosophical Society (1956–1959). Robbins was perhaps the most influential botanist in the National Academy of Sciences (NAS) during the early postwar era, and a principal participant in the plans for the global reconstruction of science.

The Robbins Papers (organized chronologically) contain correspondence, diaries, lectures (including lecture notes from B.M. Duggan's ecology course at Cornell, 1912–1915), notebooks, and photographs, covering nearly every aspect of his scientific career. Although a relatively small collection, it is an exceptionally rich source on the development of agricultural sciences, on the patronage of the life sciences by the Rockefeller Foundation, and on the political and institutional context of science.

Selected correspondence files (Box 1910–1915) include papers from his graduate years at Cornell, correspondence on plant pathology with the United States Department of Agriculture, and with the Alabama Polytechnic

Institute's agricultural school, Missouri Botanical Gardens, and the University of Wisconsin. There is material (Box 1916–1927) on plant physiology at the University of Idaho and Johns Hopkins, on World War I (correspondence with J.T. Lloyd, and Robbins's service in the Sanitary Corps), correspondence from the Agricultural Station of Delaware College, the U.S. Department of Agriculture, and on botany at Wellesley College.

The boxes dated 1927–1937 contain a wealth of information on Robbins's activities in the NRC and the Rockefeller Foundation. There are several diaries dated between 1927 and 1930, covering Robbins's scientific surveys of the life sciences for the Foundation in almost every country in Europe. These boxes also include materials on plant sciences at the University of Missouri, the University of Cincinnati, and the University of Minnesota. Boxes dated 1937–1945 contain material on the New York Botanical Garden, and a detailed account of plant sciences at the University of Wisconsin (March 31, 1944).

Robbins's expertise on international science was especially important in the postwar era, and there is interesting material on his advisory activities concerning Japan and South America (Boxes 1945–1948 and 1949–1953). Other boxes which cover the 1940s and 1950s include detailed correspondence with A.F. Blakeslee on botany and genetics, on the relation of the plant sciences to war and national needs, and on Russian science and the Lysenko affair. They also contain extensive correspondence with E.B. Wilson on activities within the OSRD and the NAS, and surveys of the effects of World War II on academic science.

Other correspondents include: G.W. Beadle, D.W. Bronk, J.M. Cattell, A. Gregg, R.G. Harrison, F.B. Jewett, J.H. Northrop**, A.N. Richards, and A. Waterman. The Flexner Papers* contain a file (1933–1935) on Robbins's activities in the NRC.

18.   Roe, Anne (1904–   ). Psychologist.
      Papers, 1953, ca. 6000 items (6 ln.ft.).

During the 1940s Anne Roe (Mrs. George Gaylord Simpson) was working on the book *The Making of a Scientist*, which was published in 1953. In it Roe tried to account for the psychological attributes—intellectual aptitude, emotional make-up, and interests—which characterized practitioners of the natural sciences, keeping their identities confidential. She collected material on 64 prominent scientists, including transcripts of interviews, Rorschach and Thematic Apperception Tests, personal data, and follow-ups she gathered over a decade later. The collection has two major limitations: 1) there is a ten-year restriction from the date of death of each scientist, thus rendering a number of files inaccessible to scholars at this time; 2) due to Roe's social biases, and the now questionable validity of some of the psychological tools she had relied on, the data and their interpretations require a critical eye. Nevertheless, within these limitations, the available files contain much valuable biographical material (including interesting anecdotes) and scientific bibliographies.

Selected files on scientists in fields related to the life sciences are: L.W. Alvarez, G.W. Beadle, J.W. Beams, J. Bonner, R.E. Cleland, G.W. Corner, E.A. Doisy, J.G. Kirkwood, K.S. Lashley, H.J. Muller, J.H. Northrop**, L. Pauling, T. Sonneborn, W.M. Stanley**, and A.H. Sturtevant.

19. Roughton, Francis John Worsley (1899–1972). Biophysicist, physiologist. Papers, ca. 1920s–1960s, ca. 90,000 items (90 ln.ft.).

The researches of the British scientist Francis J.W. Roughton on the physiology of blood and the physical biochemistry of hemoglobin are part of an intellectual tradition which included the British physiologists Joseph Barcroft, J.S. and J.B.S. Haldane, and A.V. Hill. In fact, Barcroft's and Hill's influence on Roughton was akin to mentorship. During the 1920s Roughton worked at Cambridge University on problems of oxygen diffusion in the blood, studies for which he was appointed Lecturer in Physical Biochemistry and in Physico-Chemical Physiology.

Roughton's research during the next four decades generally followed out of his work in the 1920s. That is, his early studies on diffusion were later broadened to include chemical reaction processes, theoretical and experimental analyses of factors that determine the rates of penetration of oxygen and carbon monoxide into red blood cells, and the transport of carbon dioxide in the blood. His measurements of oxygen association curves were important in elucidating the action of hemoglobin. In 1946 Roughton became chairman of the Department of Colloid Science at Cambridge, a center for research on surface chemistry and biophysical chemistry.

Roughton developed a successful research program in England, but was happier in America, where he lectured and conducted research during his extended visits. He spent much of World War II in the United States working on war projects such as carbon monoxide shock and studies in aviation medicine at the Harvard Fatigue Laboratory and the Physiological Laboratory of Columbia's Medical School; he remained associated with military research on blood physiology well past the war. In the 1950s and 1960s he also spent several semesters at the University of Pennsylvania, working closely with his colleague (and former student) Britton Chance**. Because of the close bonds that Roughton had with American science, his papers have been deposited at the APS.

This enormous collection contains notebooks, drafts of papers, manuscripts, lecture notes, calculations, laboratory manuals, annotated books from Roughton's personal library, reprints, photographs, and voluminous correspondence. The Roughton Papers document his research in Cambridge and America, his war activities, and broader aspects of physiology, biophysics, and physical biochemistry.

Having been kept close to its original arrangement, the correspondence (divided into several alphabetically arranged sections) is presently difficult to use. Roughly sketched, boxes containing files 19.00–23.20 include material related to colleagues. There is correspondence with J. Barcroft from the 1940s, material related to Roughton's activities during the war (files 19.03–19.06), long-term correspondence with his student R.L. Berger, and exchanges with J.H. Camroe at the University of Pennsylvania (files 19.11–19.23). There is extensive scientific and administrative correspondence between Roughton and Britton Chance** (files 19.43–19.44, 1940–1960s), with J.T. Edsall (files 19.51–19.52, 1940s–1960s), some material on Q. Gibson (20.33–20.80), and two letters (1924 and 1970) from A.V. Hill (file 20.78). There is interesting correspondence with L. Pauling (file 21.60, 1944–1957) and with M. Perutz (files 21.81–21.83, 1950s), two letters from Barcroft, and an important letter from W.B. Cannon* from the 1920s (file 21.91). Files 21.91–21.96 contain material on Roughton's department in the 1940s (including an interesting letter from Hill), and correspondence from the 1920s with Walter M. Fletcher; files 21.98–22.00, 22.13 document his involvement with the military.

Roughton's research on oxygen determinations in blood is reflected in the correspondence with marine physiologist P.F. Scholander (file 22.30–22.32, 1940s–1960s), with D. Van Slyke** (files 22.40–22.43, 1930s–1960s), and with J. Wyman (files 22.60–22.62, 1940s–1960s). Files 22.72–22.90 contain photographs of several noted European and American physiologists, and there is valuable correspondence in file 23.20 with F. Haurowitz on the history of hemoglobin research.

In addition to correspondence there are biographical accounts on Roughton (file 42.70), a great deal of material on the Department of Colloid Science (files 41.00–41.30), and on laboratory instruments in physiology and biophysics from the 1930s to the 1960s (file 46.60).

20. Rous, F. Peyton (1879–1970). Pathologist, virologist. APS 1939.
     Papers, ca. 1917–1970, ca. 60,000 items (60 ln.ft.).

The papers of Peyton Rous include correspondence, lectures, articles, reports, laboratory records, reprints, and photographs. These materials record in detail Rous's long scientific career and his discoveries which revolutionized several areas in the life sciences. His discovery in 1910 that viruses cause malignant tumors in fowl and his subsequent work in tumor virology linked intellectual and disciplinary trends in medical physiology and bacteriology at the turn of the century with those of molecular biology in the 1950s. The founding of the sub-specialty of tumor virology also reoriented the course of cancer research. His innovative laboratory techniques, especially in tissue culture, advanced the course of cytology and microbiology. The files on Rous (ca. 200 files, 1910s–1960s) contain annual reports, lectures, and papers describing these diverse studies.

During World War I, in collaboration with several colleagues at the Rockefeller Institute (notably Oswald H. Robertson), Rous devised methods for preserving human blood through the use of blood banks that made more transfusions possible. This important project is documented in the Oswald H. Robertson correspondence (1917–1960).

In addition to documenting his paradigmatic researches, the collection also contains hundreds of files on the *Journal of Experimental Medicine* (JEM), of which Rous was an editor from 1921 to 1970. These files contain a wealth of information on editorial policies, referee accounts, scientific controversies, and changing trends in the life sciences. Rous's broader institutional and social influence is reflected in the files on scientific institutions and organizations, including the Rockefeller Institute, the Federation of American Societies for Experimental Biology, the National Academy of Sciences, the National Research Council, and the New York Academy of Medicine.

The Rous Papers also contain material on Rous's Nobel Prize, which he received fifty-six years after his historic discovery, an interesting episode in the history of the life sciences. Rous's correspondence with several colleagues (especially with C. Andrewes), together with the boxes on the Nobel Prize, reveal aspects of the delayed recognition of his contributions, the controversies surrounding the question of whether tumors arose spontaneously or were induced, and the events leading to the final acceptance of his work.

His pioneering role in basic cancer research and his continuous leadership in the field is recorded in numerous files (ca.1920s–1960s) on the J.C. Childs Memorial Fund, the American Cancer Society, the Jackson Memorial Laboratory, and the Sloan-Kettering Institute.

The Rous correspondence is divided into two main sections: 1) personal-professional correspondence, and 2) editorial correspondence (JEM).

Some important correspondents in the first section include: A.C. Abbott (1920s) on interactions between Rous's laboratory and the University of Pennsylvania School of Hygiene and Public Health; C.L. Alsberg (1920s) on aspects of bacteriology in the United States Department of Agriculture Bureau of Chemistry; E. Altenberg (1940s), on problems of the virus theory of cancer; C. Andrews (2 files, 1930s), detailed correspondence on tumor virology; C.F. Angus (1936–1938), on political conditions in Europe; M.

Blankenhorn (1930s), administrative correspondence; J. Barcroft (1932); W.B. Cannon* (1920s), important exchanges on scientific and social aspects of research; E. Caspari (1930s), on the intellectual migration; J.M. Cattell (1930s), on Science Service; Childs Memorial Fund; A. Cohn (3 files, ca.1920), on the Rockefeller Institute; G.W. Corner (3 files, 1930s–1960s); H.R. Dean (10 files, ca. 1930s), including information on pathology in England; Euthanasia Society of America (ca. 1930s), contains information on the history of cancer research. S. Flexner* (17 files, ca. 1920–1930s), important administrative and scientific correspondence, especially on disciplinary trends, and women in science; H. Gasser (7 files, 1930s–1940s), institutional aspects, impressions on J.H. Northrop's** research; A. Gregg (4 files, 1920s–1950s), on biomedical research, the Rockefeller Foundation, and social aspects of biomedical sciences (including anti-Semitism); A. Gratia (ca. 1930s); F.B. Hanson (ca. 1930s), on the Rockefeller Foundation and physico-chemical biology; G. de Hevesy (4 files, ca. 1960s); Jackson Memorial Laboratory; K. Landsteiner* (5 files, ca. 1920s–1940s); R. Shope (ca. 1930s–1960); W. Stanley** (ca. 1930s–1960s); H. Zinsser (ca. 1920s–1930s); and R. Wyckoff** (ca. 1930s–1960s).

The editorial correspondence (selected JEM files) includes: O.T. Avery, F.M. Burnet, E. Chargaff*, S.S. Cohen, R. Dubos, S. Flexner*, F. Haurowitz, M. Heidelberger, F. Horsfall, A. Kabat, R. Lancefield, K. Landsteiner*, J. Loeb**, P. Olitsky*, L. Pauling, T.M. Rivers*, O.H. Robertson, P. Rous*, A. Sabin, J. Salk, F. Seibert*, D. Van Slyke**, G.G. Wright, R.W. Wyckoff**, H. Zinsser.

The Rous collection is complemented by 11 files (1916–1941) in the Flexner Papers* on administrative aspects of the Rockefeller Institute, on activities in professional societies, communications related to the JEM, on Flexner's* visit to Cambridge (1926–1927), and on tumor virology and protein chemistry.

21. Schultz, Jack (1904–1971). Geneticist, biochemist.
Papers, 1920–1971, ca. 25,000 items (27 1/2 ln.ft.).

Jack Schultz was the last graduate student to earn his doctorate under Thomas H. Morgan at Columbia (1929), joining his mentor at the new biology division at the California Institute of Technology (1929–1936, 1940–1942). Although trained as a geneticist, Schultz began combining classical *Drosophila* genetics with gene chemistry as early as 1930, when American genetics and biochemistry had little common ground. He also appreciated the significance of nucleic acids in heredity at a time when the protein view of the gene was dominant.

These research interests led Schultz in 1936 to a long-term collaboration with the Swedish biochemist Torbjörn Caspersson** on studies of nucleic acids in relation to genetics (a collaboration reflected in 11 files of correspondence, ca. 1930s-1970), and to Schultz's move to the Department of Genetics and Cytochemistry at the Institute for Cancer Research in Philadelphia (1943–1969). His research program was therefore an important link between classical and molecular genetics, and between pure and applied research.

Raised in New York's intellectual milieu, Schultz's temperament inclined him toward synthesis of scientific knowledge. His strength lay in organizing research and in identifying original problems and researchers. He did not enjoy writing, and did not publish or correspond prolifically; the Schultz Collection reflects this pattern in his career. There are lectures, research data, grants, and considerable material on his activities in the American Cancer Society (1945–1970), American Institute for Biological Sciences (1962–1970), American Society of Naturalists (3 files, 1963–1971), Genetics Society of America (3 files, ca. 1960s), National Institutes of Health (1951–1965), National Research Council (1933–1970), the National Academy of Sciences (1947–1957), and the Rockefeller Foundation (1934–1950). There is also material related to conferences, international congresses, and several journals in the life sciences.

Some of the major correspondents are: J. Alexander (1941–1946), on genes as colloids; G.W. Beadle (1946–1970); David Bonner (1948–1962); James Bonner (1954–1969); T. Caspersson** (11 files, 1937–1970); M. Demerec* (2 files, 1929–1966), on genetics, Cold Spring Harbor*, and molecular biology; T. Dobzhansky (3 files, 1929–1969); B. Ephrussi (1934–1968); J.B.S. Haldane (1933–1936); A. Hollaender* (1944–1969); J. Lederberg (1958–1967); B. McClintock (1942–1951); D. Mazia (1941–1970), on nucleic acids; A.E. Mirsky (3 files, 1948–1963), mostly correspondence related to the journal *The Cell*; J. Monod (1938); T.H. Morgan (2 files, 1929–1943); H.J. Muller (1941–1967); T. Sonneborn (1945–1960), scientific correspondence; C. Stern (1930–1969); K.G. Stern (1944–1951), on physico-chemical genetics; E. Sutton (1940–1943), on nucleic acids and chromosomes; E.L. Tatum (1945–1969).

22.   Seibert, Florence Barbara (1897–   ). Biochemist.
      Papers, 1920–1970s, ca. 5000 items (4 ln.ft.).

The papers of Florence Barbara Seibert—correspondence, reports, and manuscripts—afford an opportunity to learn a great deal about her work on the tubercle bacillus at the Phipps Institute of the University of Pennsylvania (1932–1959). Her fundamental studies, which combined theories and techniques of protein chemistry, microbiology, and immunology established an international standard for diagnosis of tuberculosis and led to methods for a safe use of intravenous medication and blood transfusions. The Seibert Collection also contains material on her later interest in cancer research at the Veterans' Administration Hospital in St. Petersburg, Florida. Taken together, these two research programs document interesting aspects of basic biochemical research within a medical context.

Because of its clinical relevance, Seibert's research on the tubercle bacillus was of immense interest to pharmaceutical houses. Her papers are therefore a valuable source on the cooperation between academic biochemists and the drug industries. There is correspondence with Eli Lilly Research Laboratories (2 files, 1934–1956) on supply of filtrates, and with E.R. Long (18 files, 1924–1974), which documents Seibert's work with pharmaceutical companies. The communications with Merck, Sharpe & Dohme (8 files, 1926–1968), are informative on contracts, equipment, and production, as is the correspondence with Parke-Davis & Co. (6 files, 1932–1975).

The Seibert Collection is also an important source on the history of women in science. A graduate of Goucher College (1920), Seibert received her doctorate from Yale in 1924 under Lafayette B. Mendel. She then joined H.G. Wells at the biochemistry department at the University of Chicago, where she worked until her move to the Phipps Institute in 1932. A recipient of several prestigious awards and fellowships, Seibert has been rather atypical as a woman scientist of the 1920s and 1930s in terms of recognition (though she did not attain full professorship until 1955, long after her accomplishments had established her as a leading expert in her field). A highly productive scientist, she was well connected within the international community of biochemists. She was also committed to the cause of women in science and communicated with other women working in the life sciences. The correspondence reflects her secure place in the main-stream of biochemistry, as well as her special position as a woman in science.

Some of the correspondents include: American Association of University Women (1943, 1972); American Chemical Society (4 files, 1942–1977), including material on her Garvan Gold Medal; R.J. Anderson (1934–1950); E.J. Cohn** (2 files, 1934–1947); Irene C. Diller (10 files, 1950s–1960s), scientific and personal communications; Lydia Edwards; Emily W. Emmart (1944–1945); Goucher College (6 files, 1917–1940s); Guggenheim Foundation (1930s), on Seibert's fellowship to Uppsala; M. Heidelberger (2 files, 1931–1944); F.G. Hopkins (1928–1929); K. Landsteiner* (1934–1941); E.R. Long (18 files, 1924–1974), scientific and administrative correspondence; L.B. Mendel (4 files, 1920–1934); K.O. Pedersen (1938–1973); A.N. Richards (1943–1945); Florence R. Sabin (5 files, 1933–1951), mostly scientific correspondence; J.B. Sumner (1937–1955); T. Svedberg** (2 files,

1932–1949); A. Tiselius** (5 files, 1938–1961); University of Pennsylvania (4 files, 1934–1958); H.G. Wells (1923–1943); J.W. Williams** (6 files, 1938–1948).

23. Severinghaus, Elmer Louis (1894–1980). Biochemist.
    Correspondence, 1920–1945, ca. 100 items

The scientific career of Elmer Louis Severinghaus may be divided into three main phases: 1921–1945, as professor of physiological chemistry and professor of clinical medicine at the University of Wisconsin; 1945–1958, as director of research at Hoffmann-La Roche; and 1958–1965, as professor of public health and nutrition and associate director of the Institute of Nutrition Sciences at the College of Physicians and Surgeons of Columbia University. The third phase included extensive travel to developing countries as a teacher and consultant for international projects in nutrition. After retiring, Severinghaus was chief nutritional consultant to the Church World Service. The Severinghaus Papers cover the first phase of his career: his research program in metabolism, endocrinology, and insulin physiology at the University of Wisconsin.

Although the collection is small and limited to letters written to Severinghaus, it is a helpful source on the growth of biochemistry and nutrition in an institutional context where agricultural and medical research intersected. Biochemistry, nutrition, and physiology at the University of Wisconsin developed in close cooperation with the region's food and drug industries, and the papers contain interesting correspondence on issues related to industrial research, contracts, and patents.

Selected correspondents include: Association for the Study of Internal Secretions (later renamed The Endocrine Society); H. Bradley (1920s), on physiological chemistry at Wisconsin; W.B. Cannon* (1936); T.M. Carpenter (1927), scientific correspondence; A. Carrel (1930s), scientific correspondence; K.K. Chen (1924), on Union Medical College in Peking; G.W. Corner (1940); P. de Kruif (1944); C.K. Drinker (1929), scientific and administrative correspondence; G.A. Harrop (1937), on setting up pharmaceutical research at Squibb; R.G. Hoskins (1934), on policies of the Association for the Study of Internal Secretions; E. Hume (1920), on teaching and research opportunities in biochemistry in China; A.C. Kinsey (1946), on establishing sex and behavior research at Indiana University; T.G. Klumpp (1939), on scientists as experts on policies of the Food and Drug Administration; C.D. Leake (1944), on aspects of cooperative research and Severinghaus's goals at Hoffmann-La Roche; E.M. Nelson (1942), on advisory activities for the Food and Drug Administration; A.N. Richards (1942), on activities related to CMR (Committee on Medical Research); W.H. Sebrell (1943), on the policy of the U.S. Public Health Service of adding vitamin D to milk; E. Shorr (1940), on the Symposium on Menopause; C.S. Slicher (1930), on issues of patents surrounding the cooperation between the dairy industries and biochemical nutrition at the University of Wisconsin; B. Sure (1937), on the relationship between nutrition, agriculture, and medicine; F.B. Talbot (1934), on controversies surrounding patent rights; W. Weaver (1934), on the relationship between endocrinology and behavior within the Rockefeller Foundation's program of physico-chemical biology; R.M. Wilder (1939), on insulin research; Wisconsin Alumni Research Foundation (1930s), on insulin research; R.M. Yerkes (1934), on research on endocrinology and behavior.

24. Wilson, Edmund Beecher (1856–1939). Biologist, zoologist. APS 1888. Notebooks, 4 vols.

E.B. Wilson was a highly prolific biologist and a central figure within the network of scientists (among them Flexner*, Morgan, Whitman, Lillie**, and Loeb**) who built up American biology at the turn of the century. His scientific career, first at Bryn Mawr College and then at Columbia University, evolved through three major research phases; these developments mirrored some of the wider trends in American biology as it moved from descriptive to experimental modes of inquiry. The first period, 1879–1891, was concerned with descriptive embryology, morphology, and cell lineage. The second phase, 1891–1903, focused on experimental embryology, differentiation, and artificial parthenogenesis. Between 1903 and 1938, Wilson (with frequent interactions with Morgan's *Drosophila* group nearby) directed his energies to problems of the cellular basis of heredity. His grand synthesis, *The Cell in Inheritance and Development* (1900, 1925), and the many students he trained shaped the course of experimental biology.

Wilson's papers do not seem to have been preserved, with the exception of these fragments of records from his graduate courses at Columbia. The materials include a private journal (1903–1928), a ledger containing administrative information on Columbia's department of zoology, and records of graduate students (among them A.F. Shull, J. Schultz*, H.J. Muller, C.B. Bridges, A.H. Sturtevant, R. Lancefield, and C. Stern). The various details on course enrollments, requirements, exams, and assistants, combined with Wilson's two notebooks (with observations and drawings) form a vivid record of the early period of academic biology in America. These materials are complemented by Wilson's scientific and administrative correspondence in the Flexner Papers* (3 files, 1915–1939).

Secondary Group: Manuscript Sources on Scientists in the Collections of Other Scientists

1. Svante Arrhenius (1859–1927). Chemist. APS 1911.
   Osterhout Papers*.

   Svante Arrhenius received the Nobel Prize in 1903 for his studies of electrolytic dissociation in solutions, work which was on the borderland of physics and chemistry. Two years later he assumed the directorship of the Nobel Institute for Physical Chemistry, a post he held until his death. His proclivity for interdisciplinary topics led him to apply principles from physical chemistry to immunology and to advance theories of cosmology and the origin of life (*Worlds in the Making*, 1908). His broad scientific interests and his position in the Nobel Institute placed him at the center of international communities of physical and life scientists.

   W.J.V. Osterhout* met Arrhenius at Berkeley, where Arrhenius was a visiting professor shortly after being awarded the Nobel Prize. The friendship which developed between the two men is reflected in about thirty letters (in English) written by Arrhenius (1 file, ca. 1906–1924). In these letters Arrhenius refers to his visit at Berkeley and his friendship with Jacques Loeb**, and later (1911) to his visit at the Rockefeller Institute. He conveys his impressions of science in the United States and other countries, his reflections on books and scientific issues, and gives descriptions of the research in his laboratory (1913).

   The correspondence during the war is filled with details about German science and the impact of the war on Europe's scientific community. Postwar letters describe vividly the plight of the average person, as well as the changing attitude toward German science. Of particular interest are the letters concerning the congress of physiology in Paris (from which Germans were excluded) and the politics of the Nobel Prize (ca. 1920s). These letters are a rich source on European science and on the relationships between European and American science. They also reveal a great deal about Arrhenius as a scientist, thinker, and organizer of international science.

2. Ball, Eric Glendinning (1904–1979). Biochemist.
   Clark Papers*, F.R. Sabin Papers.
   (The E.G. Ball Papers are deposited at the Countway Library, Harvard.)

   Eric G. Ball received his doctorate at the University of Pennsylvania in 1930. From 1933 until 1940 he was a research associate in W.M. Clark's* biochemistry laboratory at The Johns Hopkins Medical School, where he concentrated on studies of biological oxidations and enzymatic reactions under hormonal influence. These areas remained dominant in his research program at Harvard Medical School (from 1941), where he was professor of biological chemistry and chairman of the Division of Medical Sciences (1952–1962).

Although the amount of material on Ball at the APS is small, it is a significant source in several areas. The E.G. Ball file (1934) in the F.R. Sabin Papers contains detailed letters describing his research interests while working in Clark's* laboratory. The correspondence of Ball with Clark* (1937–1963) illuminates interesting aspects of Ball's scientific career, the intellectual content and institutional settings. The most valuable part of the correspondence is the letters written from Europe when Ball was on sabbatical leave in 1937–1938. Most of the letters are about Otto Warburg's laboratory at the Kaiser-Wilhelm Institute in Berlin, where Ball was working on determinations of oxidation-reduction potentials in the cytochrome system. These letters offer a wealth of information on the physical aspects of the laboratory, social interactions, and Warburg's personality. There are also descriptions of Ball's stay at the Harnack-Haus and his reaction to the political scene in Germany.

3. Butenandt, Adolph Friedrich Johann (1903–   ). Biochemist. Neuberg Papers*.

Adolph F.J. Butenandt made most of his seminal discoveries in reproductive biochemistry in the 1930s, while serving as director of the organic chemical laboratories at the University of Tübingen. During that decade he isolated the female sex hormone estrone, the male hormone androsterone, and the female hormone progesterone. Applying sensitive microanalyses, Butenandt deduced the chemical formula of androsterone and predicted the structure of a related compound that was synthesized shortly after. He was awarded the Nobel Prize in 1939, but forced to refuse it by the Hitler regime, he did not actually receive it until 1949.

In 1936 Butenandt was appointed director of the Kaiser-Wilhelm Institute for Biochemistry in Berlin, replacing his friend and colleague Carl Neuberg*, who had been ousted by the Nazis. Butenandt helped him set up a short-lived underground laboratory in a different part of Berlin, and remained a friend and loyal supporter until Neuberg's* death in 1956.

The Butenandt files in the Neuberg Papers* (1947–1956, in German) document the strong bond between these two important biochemists. There are references to the prewar era, but much of the correspondence addresses events after the war: Butenandt's tenure at the Kaiser-Wilhelm Institute, the state of German science, and Neuberg's* plight. These letters are an important source on Butenandt, German science, and the intellectual migration.

4. Caspersson, Torbjörn Oskar (1910–   ). Cytologist, biophysicist. APS 1974
Schultz Papers*, Lewis Papers*.

Torbjörn O. Caspersson was trained in medicine and biophysics at the University of Stockholm in the 1930s, becoming a lecturer in biochemistry at the chemistry division of the Karolinska Institute (1937–1942), and professor of medical cell research and genetics in 1944. That same year a special research institution was created, the Nobel Institute for Medical Cell Research and Genetics, which soon after was supplemented by the Wallenberg Laboratory of Experimental Cell Research; Caspersson was director of both institutions.

Although he worked within a medical institutional context, Caspersson's research program focused on fundamental aspects of cytogenetics, with a special emphasis on precise spectroscopic measurements. In the 1930s and 1940s, long before the race along the path to the double helix had begun, Caspersson promoted the genetic significance of nucleic acids. Combining his knowledge of cell biology and biochemistry with accurate spectroscopic observations of nucleic acids in living cells, Caspersson concluded in the late 1930s that nucleic acids were somehow involved in protein synthesis, an unorthodox view at a time when protein chemistry dominated the chemical approach to heredity.

Some of this important work was done during a two-year collaboration with Jack Schultz* in Stockholm. After Schultz* left abruptly at the outbreak of the war in 1939, Caspersson attempted to join W.H. Lewis's* cytology laboratory at Johns Hopkins as a Rockefeller Fellow. The Caspersson file (1939–1943) in the Lewis Papers* includes important correspondence describing his collaboration with Schultz* and his future research plans.

The collaboration with Schultz*, which grew into a life-long friendship, continued through correspondence, visits, and exchange of research assistants. The Schultz Papers* contain 11 files (1937–1970) on Caspersson with letters, lectures, and reports, describing their collaboration on genetics and nucleic acids. The pre-1950s material is of special significance, documenting Caspersson's frustrations while working against the mainstream of protein research. The files contain interesting information about other institutions of the life sciences, other research programs, and science in Europe during the war. Together, these records comprise an important chapter in the history of biochemistry, biophysics, genetics, and molecular biology.

5.   Chance, Britton (1913–   ). Biochemist. APS 1958.
Roughton Papers*, Cohn Papers*, H.A. Moe Papers.
(The Papers of Britton Chance are expected to be deposited at the APS.)

Britton Chance was educated first at the University of Pennsylvania, obtaining a doctorate in 1940. A two-year association with F.J.W. Roughton*, a specialist in the biochemistry and biophysics of hemoglobin, culminated in 1942 in a second doctorate from Cambridge University. Chance returned to the University of Pennsylvania to become professor of biophysics and biochemistry and director of the Eldridge Reeves Johnson Foundation. Under his leadership, the Department of Biophysics and Physical Biochemistry became a world center for the study of cell metabolism.

During the 1940s, Chance's research program focused mainly on enzyme kinetics of peroxidases, physico-chemical studies that elucidated in minute detail the mechanisms of formation of enzyme-substrate complexes. Broadened in scope in the 1950s, the research included the study of phosphorylation mechanisms in mitochondria and cytochromes. In general, by introducing new biochemical methods, especially sensitive photometric techniques, Chance was able to explain various physiological states of cell metabolism *in vivo*.

Some of Chance's research interests overlapped with those of his British mentor, F.J.W. Roughton*, leading to collaborations which spanned decades. These activities, as well as other shared interests, are documented in several correspondence files on Britton Chance (mainly 19.43–19.44, ca. 1940s–1960s) in the Roughton Papers*. In addition to letters, there are papers and reports written by Chance, descriptions of his research program, and the broader institutional framework in which his studies were planned. Together, these materials form a substantial record of Chance's research program at the University of Pennsylvania.

Complementing these files is the correspondence with Chance in the Cohn Papers* (3 files, ca. 1960s). Their communications generally focus on the study of biochemical reactions, and more specifically on applications of the new techniques of Nuclear Magnetic Resonance to biochemical problems.

6.   Chittenden, Russell Henry (1856–1943). Physiological chemist. APS 1904.
Sixty Years of Service in Science: an Autobiography. Microfilm, 1 reel. Original at the Sterling Library at Yale.
(The Russell H. Chittenden Papers are at Yale University Library.)

Russell Henry Chittenden is generally regarded as the father of American biochemistry, having led at Yale the country's first biochemistry department

67

(ca. 1870s–1920s). A protégé of the German biochemist Willy Kühne, Chittenden continued his mentor's research program on the action of proteolytic enzymes, at the same time adapting the work at the New Haven laboratory to local and national needs. Chittenden's research program, tied to the region's agricultural chemistry and nutrition, was noted for work on toxicology and on protein requirements in humans. During World War I Chittenden was a member of a committee in charge of nutrition and food supply to the Allies. His strongest impact was in professional and administrative activities, especially as the president of the American Physiological Society, as member of editorial boards of journals such as the *American Journal of Physiology*, the *Journal of Experimental Medicine*, and the *Journal of Biological Chemistry*, and as a prolific writer. Chittenden's autobiographical account documents his contributions within a broader context of the rise of biochemistry in America.

7.   Cohn, Edwin Joseph (1892–1953). Biochemist. APS 1949.
     Bergmann Papers*, Leonard Carmichael Papers, Flexner Papers*, Rous Papers*, Florence R. Sabin Papers, Seibert Papers*, Joseph Stokes Papers. (The Edwin J. Cohn Papers are at the Pusey Library, Harvard.)

Edwin Joseph Cohn established his research program in protein chemistry in 1920 at the department of physical chemistry of Harvard Medical School. Integrating the intellectual approaches of his mentors—L.J. Henderson, F.R. Lillie**, T.B. Osborne, and S.P.L. Sorensen—and adapting his combined program to the concerns of a medical institution, Cohn addressed a variety of physiological problems of clinical relevance. However, fundamental investigations of the physical chemistry of proteins and amino acids remained a major focus throughout his tenure at Harvard. These studies (in collaboration with J.T. Edsall, J. Kirkwood, J. Oncley, and J. Wyman) led to the discovery of important correlations between the structures of proteins and their physical properties, such as solubilities, ionization, and spectra.

     Being a central figure in the international network of protein chemists, Cohn communicated with many colleagues. There is substantial correspondence in the Bergmann Papers* (ca. 1930s–1940s) on scientific and administrative issues, including materials on the campaign to establish a separate section on protein chemistry within the American Chemical Society (see also a file on "Protein Committee", ca. 1930s). There is correspondence in the Flexner Papers* (ca. 1919–1927) regarding Cohn's liver research, scientific correspondence with Florence Sabin (ca. 1920s) in the Sabin Papers, with Florence Seibert* (2 files, 1937–1947) and with P. Rous* in their respective papers.

     One of Cohn's most important accomplishments, and a major contribution to biomedical knowledge of the Committee on Medical Research, was his blood-fractionation project. An enormous enterprise involving biochemists, physiologists, clinicians, and other life scientists, the project yielded purified serum albumin for treatment of shock, gamma globulins for immunization, and numerous other protein fractions of blood plasma. Cohn's procedures were scaled up for industrial distribution for military and civilian uses. This project also yielded new information about blood chemistry and physiology. The Joseph Stokes Papers at the APS (currently unindexed) contain a great deal of material on Cohn's war project. Some of this material may be found in the files dealing with research on gamma globulins, and in the files on the Committee for Blood Fractionation.

8. Du Vigneaud, Vincent (1901–1978). Biochemist. APS 1944.
   Bergmann Papers*, Clarke Papers*, Cohn Papers*, J.B. Murphy Papers, H.A. Moe Papers, L. Carmichael Papers, E.L. Opie Papers.
   (Oral History, 1964, at the Butler Library, Columbia University)

Most of Vincent du Vigneaud's prolific career was spent at Cornell University Medical College in New York, where his research program focused mainly on amino acids. In the late 1930s his studies of the amino acid methionine made it possible to trace the biochemical pathway through which methyl groups were shifted from compound to compound. In the early 1940s he identified the compound biotin and deduced its chemical structure; biotin was immediately synthesized by Merck Laboratories. And in the late 1940s he isolated the active fragment of the pituitary hormone oxytocin, and within a few years worked out its amino acid composition. It was the first protein hormone ever to be synthesized, earning du Vigneaud the 1955 Nobel Prize in chemistry.

    Du Vigneaud and Bergmann*, whose researches on amino acids were closely related, also shared other cultural and social interests. The Bergmann Papers* contain substantial correspondence with du Vigneaud (ca. 1930s–1940s) documenting this common ground. There is a file on du Vigneaud (ca. 1960s) in the papers of Mildred Cohn*; Cohn had worked in his laboratory from 1938–1946. There is also interesting material on du Vigneaud in the Clarke Papers* (ca. 1950s) describing his graduate student days at the University of Rochester.

9. Levene, Phoebus Aaron Theodore (1869–1940). Biochemist. APS 1923.
   Bergmann Papers*, F. Boas Papers, Flexner Papers*, J.B. Murphy Papers, P. Rous Papers*, F.R. Sabin Papers.
   (The P.A.T. Levene Papers are at the Rockefeller Archive Center.)

In 1905 P.A.T. Levene was selected by Simon Flexner* to head the biochemistry program at the newly created Rockefeller Institute for Medical Research, where Levene worked until his retirement in 1939. By the time he joined the Institute, Levene was already well into his second career. Having abandoned medicine for chemistry, he had supplemented his chemistry training at Columbia University with study in the laboratories of Edmund Drechsel, Albrecht Kossel, and Emil Fischer. From Kossel he acquired an interest in nucleic acids, which developed into a major research program at the Institute.

One of Levene's most important contributions was the isolation and identification in 1909 of the carbohydrate portion of the nucleic acid molecule. That year he showed that ribose was found in some nucleic acids (RNA), and in 1929 he identified deoxyribose in another class of nucleic acids (DNA). However, his tetranucleotide hypothesis of DNA composition was disproved in the 1940s by the work of Chargaff*. Levene was an exceptionally effective laboratory researcher, and his technical skills enabled him to carry out numerous and diverse biochemical analyses. In more than 700 publications, Levene addressed the chemistry of nucleic acids, proteins, glycoproteins, sugars, and lipids; all this was aimed at explaining basic physiological processes in a chemical language.

The Papers of Simon Flexner* include 9 files (1910–1940) which contain a wealth of information on Levene's laboratory, research reports, and personal and professional correspondence related to Levene's work, as well as to the work of other biochemists. Of special interest is the correspondence (ca. 1933) about nucleic acids research, and about Max Bergmann* and general trends in biochemistry. There is also a file on Levene (ca. 1930s) in the Bergmann Papers* containing his reaction to Bergmann's work.

10. Lillie, Frank Rattray (1870–1947). Embryologist, physiologist. APS 1916.
C.B. Davenport Papers, Flexner Papers*, H.S. Jennings Papers, Lewis Papers*, J.A. Mason Papers, J.B. Murphy Papers, Osterhout Papers*, R. Pearl Papers.
(The Frank R. Lillie Papers are at the University of Chicago Archives, and at the Marine Biological Laboratory at Woods Hole.)

The scientific path of Frank Rattray Lillie began around 1890 at the University of Chicago. Starting with descriptive morphology of cell lineage of the fresh water mussel, his research moved progressively toward an experimental, physiological, and biochemical approach to fertilization and differentiation. From 1910 to 1921 Lillie focused mainly on physiological studies of fertilization in sea urchins, work which culminated in his noted "fertilizin" theory. During that period he also began his studies of sexual differentiation in freemartins, research that led him to collaborate with biochemists and resulted in the isolation and chemical analyses of sex hormones. Under

Lillie's leadership, sex research—the physiological and biochemical studies of differentiation, development, and maturation—became a major program at the University of Chicago.

Lillie was an ardent promoter of experimental biology and general physiology. His scientific success extended far beyond the laboratory. Under his directorship (1910–1935) the biology division at the University of Chicago flourished, and his fifty-five years of leadership at the Marine Biological Laboratory at Woods Hole were crucial to that institution's development. Lillie was an influential figure in the National Academy of Sciences and the National Research Council, and helped shape the direction of the life sciences through his advisory role in the Carnegie and Rockefeller Foundations.

The Flexner Papers* contain substantial material (2 files, 1915–1938), which document some of Lillie's important administrative activities. These files in the Flexner Papers* include records related to activities at Woods Hole (1915–1938), material on Lillie's role in the Rockefeller Foundation's program of "experimental biology" (the precursor of "molecular biology"), correspondence related to the National Academy of Sciences, National Research Council, and the Science Advisory Committee (ca. 1930s). There is also interesting material on Lillie in the Osterhout Papers* (ca. 1920s–1930s), on his activities at Woods Hole and other institutions of the life sciences.

11. Link, Karl Paul (1901–1978). Biochemist.
Bergmann Papers*.

Karl Paul Link had hoped to go to medical school. Instead, with the exception of two years of post-doctoral training in Europe, his entire scientific career—undergraduate, graduate, and fifty years of research—was nurtured within the agricultural tradition of the University of Wisconsin. In retrospect, medicine benefited more from his accomplishments as an agricultural chemist than it would have from his practice of medicine. His discovery of Dicumarol (an important clinical coagulant), his procedures for isolating vitamins and other natural products of importance to nutrition, and his important contributions in carbohydrate chemistry (his specialty) exemplify his overlapping medical and agricultural concerns.

Link was also an influential teacher, in a sense a scientific cult figure. His analytical excellence and technical skills, matched by a charismatic personality and an open life-style, drew many students to his laboratory and home. Through his long academic lineage (among his students are Carl Niemann and Stanford Moore), Link's influence extended to other institutions, including Max Bergmann's* laboratory at the Rockefeller Institute.

Bergmann* and Link were colleagues and friends. Their many shared scientific, cultural, and social interests are documented in the correspondence with Link (6 files, ca. 1930–1940s). The principal importance of these files lies in the information they contain about the growth of biochemistry within an agricultural context, and the relation of Link's work to other programs. Being a renowned chemist, Link was well connected within the international community of biochemists. There is a great deal on general trends in biochemistry (including a critique of protein chemistry), and interesting exchanges related to the immigration of Neuberg* and Meyerhoff. These files are an important source on the history of biochemistry in general, and American agricultural chemistry in particular.

12. Loeb, Jacques (1859–1924). Physiologist. APS 1899.
F. Boas Papers, Clark Papers*, Flexner Papers*, H.S. Jennings Papers, J.B. Murphy Papers, Osterhout Papers*, R. Pearl Papers.
(The J. Loeb Papers are at the Library of Congress, Washington, D.C.)

The American odyssey of the German physiologist Jacques Loeb began in 1891 at Bryn Mawr College, followed by eleven years at the University of Chicago, the University of California at Berkeley, and from 1910 until his death at the Rockefeller Institute in New York; the summers were spent at the marine biological laboratories at Woods Hole and Pacific Grove.

During those years Loeb's work increasingly moved toward physico-chemical explanations of life. A materialist and an arch-determinist, Loeb's research program was based on a mechanistic conception of life. His studies of phototropism aimed at demonstrating that instincts of organisms were merely photochemical phenomena, his experiments on artificial parthenogenesis in sea urchins were undertaken in order to prove that ordinary physico-chemical agents could initiate the development of life. In his last decade, Loeb's work focused mainly on proteins as the agents of life, a unification of physiology and physiological chemistry.

Loeb's striking experimental feats captured the popular and scientific imagination; his charismatic personality and cultivated manner added to his fame. Through his work and personal style he had a profound impact on the development of a non-medical general physiology. Although Loeb preferred not to participate in administrative activities and avoided bureaucratic entanglements, he was one of the most visible scientists of his generation.

The papers of Simon Flexner* contain substantial material on Jacques Loeb (4 files, 1913–1924), covering the period of Loeb's tenure at the Rockefeller Institute. The correspondence addresses issues related to research problems: Loeb's research, as well as the scientific careers of other workers in the life sciences, for example, Otto Warburg (1915), Samuel Meltzer (1919), and Leonor Michaelis (1924). There is also correspondence related to the *Journal of General Physiology*.

The material on Loeb in the Osterhout Papers* (2 files, 1909–1922) includes correspondence from Loeb's stay at Berkeley, which is as informative on Loeb as on Berkeley and Pacific Grove. There are also interesting anecdotes of Jacques Loeb, which illuminate the man and his work. The Clark Papers* contain scientific and administrative correspondence with Loeb (1920–1922), serving mainly to illustrate Loeb's influence among biochemists and chemists.

13. Northrop, John Howard (1891–1987). Biochemist. APS 1938.
Bergmann Papers*, A.F. Blakeslee Papers, C.B. Davenport Papers, Flexner Papers*, J.B. Murphy Papers, Osterhout Papers*, O. Riddle Papers, Roe Papers*, Robbins Papers*, Rous Papers*.

John Howard Northrop, an intellectual heir to a long line of scholars, had always been intrigued by the vitalist-mechanist debate. In search of insights into the nature of life, he began his advanced training in biology with T.H. Morgan and E. Beecher Wilson* at Columbia University, but soon turned to the study of physical and biological chemistry (under J.H. Nelson), where he felt he could find exact explanations of vital processes. In 1915 Northrop joined Jacques Loeb** at the Rockefeller Institute, collaborating on a variety of projects, but his interests were increasingly moving toward the biochemistry of viruses, bacteriophage, and enzymes.

In the late 1920s and 1930s this interest developed into a major research program at the Princeton branch of the Rockefeller Institute. During these years Northrop had crystallized several proteolytic enzymes and showed some of them to be autocatalytic proteins, work that also contributed to the crystallization of the tobacco mosaic virus by his colleague W.M. Stanley**. In the late 1930s Northrop returned to studies of viruses, concentrating mainly on the biochemistry of bacteriophage. In 1946 he was awarded the Nobel Prize (shared with Stanley** and J.B. Sumner) for his work on enzymes.

In addition to his research on proteins, Northrop distinguished himself on other fronts. During World War I he had developed a microbial process for producing acetone, and during World War II, techniques for measuring mustard gas. Northrop was also Simon Flexner's* confidant; his judgment on research problems and researchers, on administrative matters and editorial issues was frequently solicited by Flexner and other members of the Institute.

Northrop's intellectual and social influence is reflected in correspondence in several collections. The Flexner Papers* contain substantial material on Northrop (4 files, 1915–1941), which include Loeb's** recommendation of Northrop to work at the Institute (1915), Northrop's report on the production of acetone (1918), his work on enzymes (1929), and scientific and administrative communications. There is interesting correspondence in the Osterhout Papers* (1934–1964), mostly in relation to the *Journal of General Physiology*, and extensive correspondence in the Rous Papers* (3 files, 1920–1940s) on a wide range of scientific and institutional matters. The exchanges with Northrop in the Bergmann Papers* (1930s–1940s) relate mainly to scientific and technical issues of protein chemistry. These manuscript sources are complemented by biographical materials gathered in the Anne Roe Collection* (currently restricted).

14. Olby, Robert Cecil (1933–   ). Historian of science.
    Papers, 1951–63, ca. 150 items.

This collection of letters, documents, and biographical information represents some of the materials Olby had gathered for his noted book *The Path to the Double Helix* (1974), material which he then deposited at the APS. Correspondents include: S. Brenner, F.H.C. Crick, M. Delbrück, R. Franklin, G. Gamow, R.M. Harriott, A.D. Hershey, S. Luria, J.H. Matthaei, M. Nirenberg, M. Meselson, L. Pauling, A. Rich, J.D. Watson. The collection includes a copy of a manuscript by Crick and Watson, "The Complementary Structure of Deoxyribonucleic Acid", presented by R.C. Olby in 1969.

15. Stanley, Wendell Merideth (1904–1971). Biochemist. APS 1940.
    A.F. Blakeslee Papers, Clark Papers*, Clarke Papers*, Demerec Papers*, L.C. Dunn Papers, Flexner Papers*, H.A. Moe Papers, Osterhout Papers*, Roe Papers*, Rous Papers*.
    (The W.M. Stanley Papers are at the Bancroft Library, Berkeley.)

W.M. Stanley joined the Rockefeller Institute in 1931. After working briefly with Osterhout*, he was transferred to the Princeton branch to set up a research project on the tobacco mosaic virus, work that focused mainly on protein chemistry. At that time virology had already grown into a major field of biomedical research, but no one had yet succeeded in isolating a single virus. Stanley's skills in bio-organic chemistry, augmented by Northrop's** cooperation, resulted in 1935 in the crystallization of the tobacco mosaic virus, a technical feat that attracted international attention. Stanley's conclusion that the reproductive material in the virus was an autocatalytic protein seemed to have solved the virus mystery, and to confirm the widespread belief in the primacy of proteins in heredity. Stanley's work, for which he had received the 1946 Nobel Prize (shared with J.B. Sumner and Northrop**), has generally been viewed as a cornerstone of molecular biology and a major landmark in the history of medicine.

The Flexner Papers* contain material (1935–1941) on Stanley's research program which illuminate its early phase; the letters in the Osterhout Papers* (1937–1953) include references to Stanley's work at Osterhout's* laboratory. There is a substantial record on Stanley in the Rous Papers* (2 files, 1930s–1960s), addressing problems in virus research and its connection to cancer studies.

The interviews with Stanley in the Roe Papers* offer a wealth of biographical information on Stanley through the 1950s. These materials are especially helpful in following up on his scientific career after he left the Rockefeller Institute in 1947 to become director of the virus research center at the University of California at Berkeley, an enormous scientific enterprise that included cancer research.

16. Svedberg, Theodor (1884–1971). Chemist. APS 1941.
Seibert Papers*.

When Theodor Svedberg became professor of physical chemistry at the University of Uppsala in 1912, colloid chemistry was a major new research area in the life sciences. Based on the premise that a colloidal or aggregate state was a fundamental property of living matter, especially of protoplasm, chemists, among them Svedberg, focused on physico-chemical studies of bio-colloids.

The goal of analyzing the aggregate properties of colloids was partly responsible for Svedberg's design of the analytical ultracentrifuge, an enormous machine that separated colloidal solutions into components based on a differential rate of sedimentation in a force field. The ultracentrifuge, designed in the 1920s in collaboration with J.W. Williams** of the University of Wisconsin, was crucial in demonstrating the macromolecular theory and became a powerful sorting and weighing device in molecular research. In 1926 Svedberg was awarded the Nobel Prize for chemistry.

Until the late 1930s Svedberg's laboratory was the only place for studies requiring ultracentrifugation; it became an international center for a wide range of researches from physical chemistry to medicine. The Seibert Papers* contain material on Svedberg and his laboratory (2 files, 1932–1949), documenting the connection between her biomedical research and Svedberg's laboratory. Her correspondence with the Guggenheim Foundation (ca. 1930s) contains material relating to her fellowship in Uppsala.

17. Tiselius, Arne (1902–1971). Chemist. APS 1964.
    Seibert Papers*, Rous Papers*, H.A. Moe Papers, J. Slater Papers.

Arne Tiselius was the protégé of Theodor Svedberg at the University of Uppsala. His dissertation on the electrophoresis of colloidal proteins (1930) was an outgrowth of Svedberg's ultracentrifuge studies. It was well known since the 1900s that proteins carried different electric charges and could therefore be separated out of mixtures by applying an electromotive force. Several biochemists before Tiselius, including Landsteiner*, Northrop**, and Michaelis, had attempted to build electrophoresis apparatus, but were hindered by technical difficulties. In 1937, partly through collaborations with these men, Tiselius substantially improved on the original design, building a sensitive and reliable apparatus which quickly became indispensable to biochemical research. He was awarded the Nobel Prize in chemistry in 1948.

     Tiselius's laboratory in Uppsala became in the late 1930s a world center for research and training in the intricate techniques of electrophoresis; among the young biochemists who came to Uppsala was Florence Seibert*. The correspondence with Tiselius in the Seibert Papers* (5 files, 1938–1961) documents the technological and social aspects of her collaboration with Tiselius and his group in Uppsala. After her return to the United States, Seibert's* correspondence with Tiselius enabled her to build her own electrophoresis equipment in 1939. She remained close to Tiselius and his family, and these scientific and social contacts are well documented in the Tiselius files.

18. Van Slyke, Donald Dexter (1883–1971). Biochemist. APS 1938.
    A.F. Blakeslee Papers, Clark Papers*, Clarke Papers*, R.I. Cole Papers, Flexner Papers*, J.B. Murphy Papers, Neuberg Papers*, E.L. Opie Papers, F.R. Sabin Papers, Roughton Papers*, Rous Papers*.
    (The D.D. Van Slyke Papers are at the Rockfeller Archive Center.)

The scientific career of Donald D. Van Slyke was spent at the Rockefeller Institute for Medical Research. Beginning in 1907 in the biochemistry laboratory of P.A.T. Levene**, Van Slyke went on to become chief chemist of the hospital of the Institute, where he stayed until his move to the Brookhaven National Laboratory in 1949.

     Undoubtedly influenced by his medical environment, Van Slyke's research program in physical biochemistry focused on studies of gas, fluid, and acid-base equilibria in relation to pathology. One of Van Slyke's chief interests was the analysis of physico-chemical equilibria in blood. In collaboration with L.J. Henderson, Van Slyke developed a series of studies on the acid-base properties of hemoglobin. In these and other biomedical investigations Van Slyke relied heavily on accurate measurements, employing instruments and analytical techniques he had devised, notably his manometric apparatus for blood-gas analysis.

Van Slyke's interest in blood equilibria and in instrumentation overlapped with those of F.J.W. Roughton*. The Roughton Papers* contain correspondence with Van Slyke (files 22.40–22.43, ca. 1930s–1960s) on their shared technical and theoretical interests. The Clark Papers* contain material (3 files, 1923–1955), which reflect the common ground (intellectual and institutional) between Clark's research on physiological equilibria and the studies of Van Slyke, and their long-term professional association.

The Flexner Papers* contain a wealth of information on Van Slyke (7 files, 1913–1942). Some of the correspondence concerns the move from Levene's** laboratory to the Institute's hospital (1913), other career decisions, Van Slyke's editorship of the *Journal of Biological Chemistry* (1915–1925), and personal matters.

19. Wieland, Heinrich Otto (1877–1957). Chemist.
Neuberg Papers*, Clark Papers*.

Heinrich O. Wieland spent his student and research career at the University of Munich. His diverse researches in organic chemistry drew students from many countries; several Americans obtained advanced training in his laboratory. His most important investigations (1910s) centered on elucidating the molecular structures of bile acids, showing them to be steroid in nature. As the appreciation for the importance of steroids in reproductive physiology and in nutrition increased during the 1920s, the contributions of Wieland assumed far greater significance. He was awarded the Nobel Prize in 1927.

In the 1930s Wieland openly opposed the Nazi regime and supported his Jewish colleagues. One of them was Carl Neuberg*, who in 1937 was fired from his post as director of the Kaiser-Wilhelm Institute for Biochemistry. The Wieland correspondence (1946–1955, in German) in the Neuberg Papers contains long letters about German and American colleagues, German and American science, and exchanges about the effects of the war. The correspondence in the Clark Papers* dates from the 1920s.

20. Williams, John Warren (1898–   ). Chemist.
Bergmann Papers*, Seibert Papers*.

John W. Williams's most important contribution to chemistry lay in his design and construction of laboratory apparatus. The theoretical and experimental research on the ultracentrifuge and electrophoresis facilitated major advances in almost every field in the life sciences, especially in biochemistry, immunology, and molecular biology. Beginning around 1922 at the University of Wisconsin, Williams collaborated with the Swedish chemist Theodor Svedberg** (during Svedberg's visit to Wisconsin as a Rockefeller Fellow) on the first prototype of the ultracentrifuge. The mathematical theories behind the apparatus were worked out by the physicist Warren Weaver, who left Wisconsin to become the director of the Rockefeller Foundation's division of natural sciences. Williams's ultracentrifuge projects received sizable grants from the Rockefeller Foundation, and his laboratory was the first academic center in America to house an ultracentrifuge (1937), thus becoming an important research and training center in the life sciences.

The Seibert Papers* contain considerable material (6 files, 1938–1948) on Williams. Having purchased an ultracentrifuge in 1938, she carried on extensive correspondence with Williams related to that technology, as well as about her newly acquired electrophoresis apparatus. During the war Williams engaged in the blood fractionation project (designed by E.J. Cohn**) for preparing globulins and serum albumins. The Seibert Papers* document interesting aspects of that important project. There is also minor correspondence (4 items, ca. 1930s) in the Bergmann Papers*.

21. Wyckoff, Ralph W.G. (1897–   ). Biophysicist.
Bergmann Papers*, Flexner Papers*, J.B. Murphy Papers, Rous Papers*, J. Slater Papers.

The move of Ralph W.G. Wyckoff from the Geophysical Laboratory of the Carnegie Institution of Washington to the Rockefeller Institute in 1927 marked an important development in the history of both the Institute and American biophysics. Under Wyckoff's leadership a new subdivision was formally designated as biophysics. Wyckoff initiated his program with the study of x-ray crystallography of simple inorganic and organic molecules with an eye to determining the molecular structures of complex macromolecules such as proteins. Together with Robert B. Corey (who joined L. Pauling's group at Caltech when Wyckoff left the Institute in 1937) they laid some of the early foundations for determining the structures of amino acids.

During the 1930s, Wyckoff in collaboration with several members of the International Health Division of the Rockefeller Foundation designed an air-driven ultracentrifuge, far simpler and cheaper than the machine built by T. Svedberg**. The domestic ultracentrifuge was especially important to the virus studies of W.M. Stanley**. Wyckoff also collaborated with Rous* and J.B. Murphy in the 1930s on electromagnetic methods of isolating microphages.

The significance of Wyckoff's research transcends his technical accomplishments. Wyckoff was a champion of the new field of biophysics, and made a deliberate effort to define and shape it. The Flexner Papers* contain material (5 files, 1926–1937) which address both the technical and disciplinary aspects of the new biophysics. There is correspondence on x-ray crystallography and viruses, and an informative report on the future of biophysics. There is also material in the Rous Papers* on Wyckoff and the growth of biophysics (2 files, 1930s–1960s), and minor correspondence (5 items, ca. 1930s) in the Bergmann Papers*. These materials should be of value in reconstructing the convoluted history of American biophysics.

PUBLISHED SOURCES CONSULTED FOR THE ANNOTATIONS

Books:

Abir-Am, P., and Outram, D., eds. *Uneasy Careers and Intimate Lives: Women in Science, 1789–1979.* New Brunswick: Rutgers University Press, 1987.

Allen, Garland E. *Life Science in the Twentieth Century.* New York: John Wiley and Sons, Inc., 1975.

Asimov, Isaac. *Asimov's Biographical Encyclopedia of Science and Technology.* New York: Doubleday & Company, Inc. 1972.

Baxter, James P., III. *Scientists Against Time.* New York: Little Brown, and Co., 1946.

Bearman, David, Edsall, John, and Kohler, Robert E. *Archival Sources in Biochemistry and Molecular Biology.* Philadelphia: American Philosophical Society, 1980.

Benison, Saul. *Tom Rivers: Reflection on a Life in Medicine and Science, An Oral History Memoir.* Cambridge: M.I.T. Press, 1967.

—————, Barger, A.C., and Wolfe, E.L. *Walter B. Cannon; the Life and Times of a Young Scientist.* Cambridge: Harvard University Press, 1987.

Berenblum, Isaac. *Man Against Cancer: The Story of Cancer Research.* Baltimore: Johns Hopkins University Press, 1952.

Callahan, Raymond E. *Education and the Cult of Efficiency.* Chicago: University of Chicago Press, 1962.

Catlett, J. Stephen. *A New Guide to the Collections in the Library of the American Philosophical Society.* Philadelphia: American Philosophical Society, 1987.

Corner, George W. *A History of the Rockefeller Institute*. New York: Rockefeller Institute Press, 1964.

Crane, Diana. *Invisible Colleges: Diffusion of Knowledge in Scientific Communities*. Chicago: University of Chicago Press, 1976.

Daniels, George H. *Science in American Society*. New York: Alfred A. Knopf, 1971.

Dictionary of Scientific Biography. New York: Scribners, 1970–1980.

Dubos, René J. *The Professor, the Institute, and DNA*. New York: Rockefeller University Press, 1976.

Dupree, A. Hunter. *Science in the Federal Government*. Baltimore: Johns Hopkins University Press, 1984.

Fleming, Donald and Bailyn, Bernard. *The Intellectual Migration: Europe and America, 1930–1960*. Cambridge: Harvard University Press, 1969.

Fosdick, Raymond B. *The Story of the Rockefeller Foundation*. New York: Harper and Brothers, Publishers, 1952.

Fruton, Joseph S. *Molecules and Life*. New York: John Wiley and Sons, Inc., 1972.

—————. *A Bio-bibliography to the History of the Biochemical Sciences since 1800*. Philadelphia: American Philosophical Society, 1982.

—————. *A Supplement to the Bio-bibliography to the History of the Biochemical Sciences since 1800*. Philadelphia: American Philosophical Society, 1985.

Geison, Gerald L., ed. *Physiology in the American Context, 1850–1940*. Washington, D.C.: American Physiological Society, 1987.

Glass, H. Bentley. *An Annotated Bibliography of Manuscript Sources on Genetics in the Library of the American Philosophical Society*. Philadelphia: American Philosophical Society, 1988.

Gray, George W. *Science at War*. New York: Harper and Brothers, 1943.

Greenberg, Daniel. *The Politics of Pure Science*. New York: The New American Library, 1967.

Haber, Samuel. *Efficiency and Uplift: Scientific Management in the Progressive Era, 1890–1920*. Chicago: University of Chicago Press, 1964.

Harden, Victoria A. *Inventing the NIH: Federal Biochemical Research Policy, 1887–1937*. Baltimore: Johns Hopkins University Press, 1986.

Hughes, Sally S. *The Virus: A History of the Concept*. New York: Science History Publications, 1977.

Jackson, J.C., and Borden, C.M., eds. *The Muses Flee Hitler: Cultural Transfer and Adaptation, 1930–1945*. Washington, D.C.: Smithsonian Institution Press, 1983.

Jacob, François. *The Logic of Life: A History of Heredity*. New York: Pantheon Books, 1982.

Judson, Horace F. *The Eighth Day of Creation*. New York: Simon and Schuster, 1979.

Kargon, Robert H., ed. *The Maturing of American Science*. Washington, D.C.: American Association for the Advancement of Science, 1974.

Keller, Evelyn Fox. *A Feeling for the Organism: The Life and Work of Barbara McClintock*. New York: W.H. Freeman and Company, 1983.

—————. *Reflections on Gender and Science*. New Haven: Yale University Press, 1985.

Kohler, Robert E. *From Medical Chemistry to Biochemistry*. Cambridge: Cambridge University Press, 1982.

Ludmerer, Kenneth M. *Eugenics and American Society*. Baltimore: The Johns Hopkins University Press, 1972.

Manning, Kenneth R. *A Black Apollo of Science*. New York: Oxford University Press, 1983.

Miller, Margaret. *A Guide to Selected Files of the Professional Papers of Simon Flexner at the American Philosophical Society Library*. Philadelphia: American Philosophical Society Library, 1979.

Monod, Jacques and Borek, Ernest, eds. *Of Microbes and Life*. New York: Columbia University Press, 1971.

Mulkay, M. and Knorr-Cetina, K.D., eds. *Science Observed: Perspectives on the Social Study of Science*. London: Sage Publishers, 1983.

Mullins, Nicholas C. *Social Networks among Biological Scientists*. New York: Arno Press, 1980.

Noble, David F. *Forces of Production*. New York: Alfred E. Knopf, 1984.

Olby, Robert C. *The Path to the Double Helix*. London: Macmillan Press, 1974.

Oleson, Alexandra and Voss, John, eds. *The Organization of Knowledge in Modern America*. Baltimore: Johns Hopkins University Press, 1976.

Patterson, James. *The Dread Disease: Cancer and Modern American Culture*. Cambridge: Harvard University Press, 1987.

Paul, William E., ed. *Fundamentals of Immunology*. New York: Raven Press, 1977.

Pauly, Philip J. *Controlling Life, Jacques Loeb and the Engineering Ideal in Biology*. New York: Oxford University Press, 1987.

Pickens, Donald K. *Eugenics and the Progressives*. Nashville: Vanderbilt University Press, 1958.

Reingold, Nathan, ed. *The Sciences in the American Context: New Perspectives*. Washington, D.C.: Smithsonian Institution Press, 1979.

Reingold, Nathan and Reingold, Ida, eds. *Science in America: A Documentary History, 1900–1939*. Chicago: University of Chicago Press, 1981.

Rosenberg, Charles E. *No Other Gods*. Baltimore: Johns Hopkins University Press, 1976.

Rossiter, Margaret W. *Women Scientists in America: Struggles and Strategies to 1940*. Baltimore: The Johns Hopkins University Press, 1982.

Rupke, Nicholas, A., ed. *Vivisection in Historical Perspective*. New York: Croom Helm, 1987.

Starr, Paul. *The Social Transformation of American Medicine*. New York: Basic Books, Inc., 1982.

Williams, Greer. *Virus Hunters*. New York: Alfred A. Knopf, 1960.

Articles and Dissertations:

Abir-Am, Pnina. "The Discourse of Physical Power and Biological Knowledge in the 1930s: Reappraisal of the Rockefeller Foundation's 'Policy' in Molecular Biology," *Social Studies of Science* 12 (1982): 341–382.

—————. "From Biochemistry to Molecular Biology: DNA and the Acculturated Journey of the Critic of Science Erwin Chargaff," *History and Philosophy of the Life Sciences* 2 (1980): 3–60.

Brink, Frank, Jr. "Detlev Wulf Bronk," *Memoirs of the National Academy of Sciences* 50 (1975): 3–40.

Cross, Stephen J. and Albury, William R. "Walter B. Cannon, L.J. Henderson, and the Organic Analogy," *Osiris* 3 (1987): 165–192.

Edsall, John T. "Blood and Hemoglobin: The Evolution of Knowledge of Functional Adaptation in a Biochemical System," *Journal of the History of Biology* 5 (1972): 205–257.

—————. "Hemoglobin and the Origins of the Concept of Allosterism," *Federation Proceedings* 39 (1980), 226–235.

Fitzgerald, Deborah K. "The Business of Breeding: Public and Private Development of Hybrid Corn in Illinois, 1890–1940," Ph.D. dissertation, University of Pennsylvania, 1985.

Glass, H. Bentley. "A Century of Biochemical Genetics," *Proceedings of the American Philosophical Society* 109 (1965): 230–232.

Greenberg, Daniel S. "American Institute of Biological Sciences," *Science* 139 (1963): 319.

Karl, Barry D. and Katz, Stanley N. "The American Private Philanthropic Foundations and the Public Sphere, 1890–1930," *Minerva* 19 (1981): 236–270.

Kay, Lily E. "W.M. Stanley's Crystallization of the Tobacco Mosaic Virus, 1930–1940," *Isis* 77 (1986): 450–472.

—————. "The Tiselius Electrophoresis Apparatus and the Life Sciences, 1930–1945," *History and Philosophy of the Life Sciences* 10 (1988): 51–72.

Kevles, Daniel J. "The National Science Foundation and the Debate over Postwar Research Policy, 1942–1945," *Isis* 68 (1977): 18.

—————. "George Ellery Hale, the First World War, and the Advancement of Science in America," *Isis* 59 (1968): 427–437.

Kimmelman, Barbara N. "A Progressive Era Discipline: Genetics at American Agricultural Colleges and Experimental Stations, 1900-1920," Ph.D. dissertation, University of Pennsylvania, 1987.

Kohler, Robert E. "The Enzyme Theory and the Origins of Biochemistry," *Isis* 64 (1973): 181–196.

—————. "A Policy for the Advancement of Science: The Rockefeller Foundation, 1924–1929," *Minerva* 16 (1978): 480–515.

—————. "Innovation in Normal Science: Bacterial Physiology," *Isis* 76 (1985): 162–181.

—————. "Science, Foundations, and American Universities in the 1920s," *Osiris* 3 (1987): 135–164.

Liebenau, Jonathan. "Medical Science and Medical Industry, 1890–1929: A Study of Pharmaceutical Manufacturing in Philadelphia," Ph.D. dissertation, University of Pennsylvania, 1981.

Maienschein, Jane. "History of Biology," *Osiris* 1 (1985): 147–162.

Mazumdar, Pauline H.M. "The Antigen-Antibody Reaction and the Physics and Chemistry of Life," *Bulletin of the History of Medicine* 48 (1974): 1–21.

Owens, Larry. "Pure and Sound Government: Laboratories, Playing Fields, and Gymnasia in the Nineteenth-Century Search for Order," *Isis* 76 (1985): 182–194.

Price, Derek de S. and Beaver, D. "Collaboration in an Invisible College," *American Psychologist* 21 (1968): 1011–1018.

Reingold, Nathan. "On Not Doing the Papers of Great Scientists," *British Journal of History of Science* 20 (1987): 29–38.

————. "Vannevar Bush's New Deal for Research, or the Triumph of the Old Order," *Historical Studies in the Physical Sciences* 17 (1987): 299–344.

Rhees, David J. "The Chemists' Crusade: The Rise of An Industrial Science in Modern America, 1907–1922," Ph.D. dissertation, University of Pennsylvania, 1987.

Rogers, Naomi. "Screen the Baby Swat the Fly: Polio in the Northeastern United States, 1916," Ph.D. dissertation, University of Pennsylvania, 1986.

Roland, Alex. "Science and War," *Osiris* 1 (1985): 247–272.

Swann, John P. "The Emergence of Cooperative Research Between American Universities and the Pharmaceutical Industry, 1920–1940," Ph.D. dissertation, University of Wisconsin, 1985.

Index

87

88

Office of Naval Research (ONR) 29, 50
Office of Scientific Research and Development (OSRD) 23, 24, 27, 28, 38, 55
Olby, R.C. 74
Olitsky, P.K. 12, 13, 16, 18, 19, 26, 28, 32, 45, 50, 51, 59
Opie, E.L. 18, 69, 76
Osterhout, W.J.V. 4, 7–9, 15, 16, 18, 20, 26, 36, 45, 51–53, 64, 70–75
Pacific Grove 51–52, 72, 73
Page, W.H. 43
Park, E.A. 40
Parke-Davis 21, 27, 28, 38
Parker, G.H. 52
patents 21, 62, 63
pathology 4, 6, 8, 12, 18, 19, 44, 54, 59, 76
Pauling, L. 36, 39, 56, 57, 59, 74, 78
Pedersen, K.O. 61
peer review 30
Pepper, W. 40
Perutz, M. 36, 47, 57
pharmaceutical industries 21, 27
Phipps Institute 4, 12, 60, 61
physical chemistry 10, 18, 39, 41, 42, 46, 52, 64, 68, 75
physiological chemistry 7, 39, 62, 72
physiology 3, 4, 7–9, 11–15, 17, 18, 20, 21, 23, 25–27, 30, 37, 43, 45, 47, 51, 52, 55–58, 62, 64, 69, 71, 72, 77
Pirie, N.W. 39
plant physiology 9, 26, 27, 52, 55
polio vaccine 31–32
poliomyelitis 32, 51, 53, 54
Pollock, M.R. 39
Princeton, New Jersey 18, 73, 74
protein 10, 11, 18, 22, 35, 36, 38, 41, 59, 61, 66, 68, 69, 70, 72–76, 78
Protein Committee 36, 68
radiation 13, 14, 46, 47
radiation genetics 14, 15, 29, 43, 46, 47
Reichenstein, T. 39
reproductive physiology 77
respiration 4, 10, 13
Rich, A. 74
Richards, A.N. 21, 23, 40, 55, 62
rickettsia 38
Rittenberg, D. 39
Rivers, T.M. 8, 12, 13, 18, 23, 28, 31, 32, 45, 47, 51, 53, 54, 59